Love Your Curves

Dr Pierre Dukan

Love Your Curves

Dr Dukan Says Lose Weight Not Shape

HODDER &
STOUGHTON

Published as *Les hommes préfèrent les rondes* by J'ai Lu in France in 2008

First published in Great Britain in 2012 by Hodder & Stoughton
An Hachette UK company

3

A CIP catalogue record for this title is available from the British Library

Trade Paperback ISBN 9781444757835
Ebook ISBN 9781444757842

Translated by Morag Jordan

Typeset in Celeste by Hewer Text UK, Ltd

Printed and bound by Clays Ltd, St Ives plc

Hodder & Stoughton policy is to use papers that are natural, renewable
and recyclable products and made from wood grown in sustainable
forests. The logging and manufacturing processes are expected to
conform to the environmental regulations of the country of origin.

Hodder & Stoughton Ltd
338 Euston Road
London NW1 3BH

www.hodder.co.uk

Contents

I dedicate this book to my wife Christine, who without realizing it inspired me to write it. To Maya and to Sacha, to Sacha and to Maya, who owe their existence to the beauty and the curves of their mother and without whom my life would have so much less meaning. And to the poet Jean-Marc Natel, because without him this book would still be lying in a drawer in my desk.

Prologue

For any author, choosing the title for a book is always a decisive moment because with a few revealing words you have to sum up the argument you spend two to three hundred pages developing.

So, when I wrote the French title *Les hommes préfèrent les rondes* (*Men love women with curves*) this is a euphemism and I should have added to it, but did not have the space, that actually they never had any choice in the matter. And my whole argument is basically contained in this short additional sentence.

As the person holding this book in your hand, you may intuitively sense straightaway whether you agree or disagree with such a generalized statement. However, there are bound to be some men and women among you who will think that I have strayed – and probably for some it feels more like breaking and entering – a little too quickly into the realm of their most private predilections, and that diversity of opinions and attractions hardly lends itself to such a sweeping generalization.

If you did react this way, it would prove that you instinctively place such predilections right at the heart of sexuality and feel that nobody else is entitled to express any judgement about tastes as personal as these on your behalf.

So as to avoid any misunderstanding, I must point out to you straightaway that this book's central theme works on a different level and is not concerned with personal choice or predilection. What I am setting out to do is identify a characteristic and way of behaving that are unique to the human race.

When we talk about sexuality, we always tend to restrict our comments to human sexuality. However, whenever a biologist or a zoologist takes an objective look at the great plethora of species alive today or that have lived on earth, it is impossible not to notice that by inventing the two sexes, male and female, Mother Nature had a marvellous stroke of inspiration and found a way for each one of these species to work inescapably and unconsciously to ensure its own reproduction.

Whatever the species under scrutiny, human beings included, for the male sex and the female sex to be able to play out their respective roles, they must always possess the following three universal characteristics:

1. The two sexes must not look alike. They should be poles that are as different from each other as is possible.
2. Each difference must be a sign that automatically identifies the gender of the person or creature giving out the sign.

2

3. The more marked this difference is, the greater its magnetism and the more attractive it will be to the partner of the opposite sex.

This way of behaving can be applied to all sexual animals that live on earth. It is a straightforward biological inevitability and to suggest that the animals concerned have any free will would be utterly ludicrous. By way of example, nobody would ever dream of pondering upon whether a lioness prefers her lion with or without his mane.

If the history of human pride could be written down, we would realize that its main theme has always been our refusal to humbly admit that we too belong to the rest of the animal kingdom.

However, our modern times have blown open a breach in this rampart of contempt, forcing us to admit that there really is a 'human nature' which also has to submit to the general laws of the living world.

So our species is no exception to the rule. It has its two sexes and they have certainly operated just as effectively as every other species since, two million years after the arrival of humankind, I am here as one of its modest representatives writing these lines. And in the wake of this incontestable evidence comes proof of the differences between the sexes and, most importantly, the natural power of attraction these differences have.

The purpose of this book is to explore and investigate one of these differences. A very specific characteristic that has always been a sign of womanhood – I am refer-ring to women's curves.

To avoid any possible confusion, and to identify this characteristic as accurately as possible, I would like to point out that I will definitely not be looking at weight, plumpness and certainly not obesity. Weight and fat are neutral attributes that have no sexual impact and they are found just as commonly in men, children and animals.

The curves I am talking about are a special roundness that is a distinctive feature of woman and are found very specifically on her hips, her thighs, her breasts, in the curve of her knee and the contours of her face.

I am claiming therefore, by virtue of one of the most elementary rules of universal sexual life, that these curves are one of the differences that set the human female apart. That in fact they are even one of the human female's best signals. And, based on the same logic as the living world, I draw the conclusion that this highly distinctive characteristic can only be highly attractive.

If I thought this statement was all I needed to give you, then my book would have fitted into a single page. However, we are constitutionally short-sighted and we live with our noses so pressed up against the glaringly obvious that we do not even notice what is staring us in the face. So this statement needed to be elaborated and the evidence scrutinized.

To do this I had to start off by exploring a field that is still very much in the hands of researchers, namely the field of non-verbal communication. This is the only communication the rest of the animal world uses and yet man constantly attempts to refuse to acknowledge it, but to no avail.

So I have called a few animals to the witness box, ones that I have deliberately selected from species that communicate in a very expressive way using specific senses: birds for sound, rats for smell, and fish for sight. We only have to watch them communicate sexually to realize everything that we owe to them.

However, what we share in common with animals should not make us forget what is unique about our own species' sexuality. For a long time woman hesitated before emerging from her ape-like legacy, and then all of a sudden, thanks to providential mutations, she stood upright and became the first female creature on earth to make love from the front. Her breasts, her hips and her thighs made their appearance and, so as not to spoil the display, her hair disappeared.

This is the most wonderful story I know. Once revealed, there can be no doubt about why the female body filled out so harmoniously. And when faced with these magical attributes, we can no longer close our eyes of our own free will.

However, the inexplicable still has to be explained. For eighty thousand generations, males have adored women's curves, so much so that they have been at women's 'beck and call', so how could two successive generations have taken it upon themselves to reject such an enormous advantage? How has the taboo on curves managed to infiltrate a bastion that is so biologically protected?

I have to confess to you that it has not been easy. The cultural forces that waged battle had to be particularly violent; and yet it has all taken place silently and covertly. The collective feminine subconscious must be especially well sound proofed.

As tempted as I may feel, I cannot say more to you about this and reveal here and now who was waging the war. To bring the people really responsible back up to the surface, I have had to dig right down into the hidden workings of our Western culture and, once there, I realized that this current ban on curves was only one of the cogs in a conspiracy that now threatens to narrow the gap between the sexes.

Subconsciously, our civilization is acclaiming a dictate which tends to make men like women and make women like men.

Once a species has become sufficiently weakened that it allows itself to be tempted by precepts as corrosive as these, you do not need to be a genius to sense decadence in the air.

However, if women have gone along with the idea of being 'amputated' in this way, I do not believe that nature has given them the means of making their wishes come true. And men know full well that, rather than losing weight, far more often these women end up suffering.

Prologue

With these men, and for these men, I want to believe that common sense, or at the very least our most elementary instinct of self-preservation, will never stop men from loving women with curves.

Part One

WOMEN'S CURVES AND NATURE

In 1850, there was not a soul on earth who believed men and apes were related. Today, we can no longer be in any possible doubt about it. However, it is funny to see how we have taken on board this earth-shattering truth in an abstract way, a little like a child learning a formula by rote and accepting it as true because a respected schoolmaster has said so.

The collective consciousness has not drawn any conclusion from it. A few researchers, biologists and ethologists are the only ones digging down deep into man's animal nature and their discoveries, which smack a little of heresy, are always difficult to present to the general public. Up until now, the greatest of all these scandals has broken only in the very enclosed field of social sciences. Yet it contains a charge that is so explosive that people, known for being wise and calm, are clashing with one another in a proper war of religion.

So what then is this scandal?

Quite simply it is about a reversal of priorities. Previously, the mind alone was deemed as human. Our animal nature and our instincts were considered to be vestiges that had vanished with the miracle of intelligence and language. Ever since religions and philosophies have existed, this opinion was taken to be a truth.

The biologist bombshell reveals, with evidence to prove it, that what decides, motivates and gives us reasons for living and not dying, what drives us to love, to desire, to fight or take flight; our anxieties, our emotions, our fascinations, our need to venerate idols or gods – all this comes purely and simply from our animal nature. The mind and reason are wonderful tools for adaptation but are rarely used for making decisions and far less in motivating us. In the best case scenario, these tools enable us to explain ourselves and find ways of achieving our desires. In the worst case scenario, they camouflage our desires or they stand in their way.

This revelation is profoundly disconcerting for spiritualists who rule supreme over social sciences and is inevitably leading to agonized re-examination.

However, the revelation is best illustrated in sexual communication. When man and woman left their animal state behind they had no language and yet they must have been able to communicate effectively since we are here today discussing the matter. Nowadays we talk in such a sophisticated way that it might appear absurd to have preserved these primitive exchanges. And yet, this is exactly how it is. When a man feels attracted to a woman to the extent that he wants to be her partner, a dual narrative goes on inside him.

There is the conscious narrative, the one you know as well as I do, and a superficial parade of sound, coherent reasons peppered with logic, and decisive arguments. Nevertheless, it is only through the hidden, and therefore subconscious, narrative that the magnetic forces of attraction operate and that decisive choices become apparent. Yet what is most disquieting, and I am almost ashamed to mention it, is that these decisions, on which often so much depends, are simply responses to a multitude of biological signals that are not particularly noticeable and only our sense organs can perceive.

At the present time, not all these messages are known but they are currently being recorded. They mainly play out on four registers:

1. The visual register that perceives shapes and contrasts, gestures and the most expressive behaviour.
2. The olfactory register with an unknown world of smells that turn out to be even more personalized than our fingerprints. Biologists assure us that as love develops between a couple, these smells play a decisive role in fixing upon and marking out a partner.
3. The auditory register with its ability to grasp the whole message of something as marvellous and complex as the human voice with its timbre, its warmth and its emotional content, going far beyond any analysis can to explain why certain voices either attract or repel us.

4. Finally there is the tactile register, which explains how people blind from birth can achieve impressive feats of communication and which one day will allow us to understand such disconcerting sayings as 'having some one under your skin'.

This cocktail of smells, shapes and textures may appear trivial to you. However, I can guarantee you that it is this cocktail that decides, that sets in motion the process that will result in love if, as is highly likely in this case, the respective orgasms climax together.

Everything else is just verbiage, false reasons and alibis. We will talk about the right education, qualifications, good dress sense, intelligence, culture, religions, nice manners and so on. But all these niceties have never won the argument. So we then turn to a magical word – 'charm'. And with it comes the greatest and most innocent of all confessions. Charm does not mean anything. Charm has no rational meaning. Quite simply it expresses the fact that the cocktail has worked and that it worked precisely where it was meant to work. This charm is, however, subtle; it works totally subconsciously and discreetly, giving the intellect complete centre stage so that it gets all the glory.

Women's curves are very much one of the ingredients in this cocktail. I even believe that they are the main one. Only natural and sexual scent may at times vie for first place.

So how can we explain the fact that since the 1960s our Western civilization has imposed a taboo on women's curves and an even stricter taboo concerning smells? Are not unisex jeans and chemical deodorants the most telling symbols of how shape and smell are being expunged?

It is difficult to escape the logical conclusion that what is really going on here is a genuine attempt at sabotage. In the second part of this book I will not hold back on this topic. For the time being, though, you need to be given the facts and proof that will persuade you that this amazing cocktail actually exists.

Even if you do not particularly like animals, please be patient and read the following pages carefully. You are not being taken off on some pointless detour, because there is a little of us in their instinctive reactions and the non-verbal language that holds the key to our basic motives and urges.

1. Non-verbal communication in the animal world

When a dog wags its tail, it is sending out a signal that it is friendly and good-natured. The dog cannot control this movement as it is totally subconscious. However, the tail-wagging has a purpose and, if intended for another dog, it will be understood this way. The other dog will no doubt react likewise and both dogs will end up playing together without there being any aggression.

Whenever a cat moves its tail, it is sending out a signal of hostility and a child who persists in teasing the cat could well end up wishing they hadn't. Another cat would, however, instinctively sense the hostility and prepare either for fight or flight.

These two examples prove that the same signal may well mean something different according to the conventions specific to each species. What they have in common is the way in which they work. Signals such as these are being transmitted throughout the animal kingdom. Konrad Lorenz, the Nobel Prize-winning animal behaviourist, calls them 'triggers'. They are decoded by the creatures that receive them and they stimulate instincts shared by all species. We are not exempt from this process and women's curves are one of the most expressive messages that men are tempted to respond to.

Our sensual repertoire is another universal link that we share with the rest of the living world. Bar a few rare exceptions, everything that is alive on the planet sends out signals that can be picked up by the five senses. Each species has its own particular preference. Man has deliberately chosen sight and hearing, enabling us to become audiovisual masters. Nonetheless, and blind people provide us with clear proof of this, we also respond to smell, touch and taste. It is perhaps true that, as we have evolved, their potential has become partially atrophied but what does remain of them has been discredited and repressed. Rest assured, though, that they keep on working away, whether we like it or not.

In this chapter I have drawn upon a few examples of animals whose means of communication are restricted to one specific sense, as this will provide more accurate proof. It is absolutely vital that you understand this mechanism because once the time comes for us to cross the Rubicon separating man from the other animal species many mysteries will lose their substance. It will then be time to behold women's curves through new eyes and bestow upon them their true meaning.

Olfactory communication: smells as messages

The world of odours is the oddest world there is, and especially so for man as he perceives smell with the most primitive parts of his brain. Very widely held opinion would have us believe that this is an area we are missing out on and that our sense of smell has wasted away.

This is in part correct and to be persuaded of it we only need take a look at what police sniffer dogs can do – a mere whiff of a handkerchief and off they go for miles, tracking a fleeing criminal.

Nevertheless, although we have lost out on quantity we still retain quality. The tragedy is that we are totally unaware of the olfactory experiences we have.

This means we gain impressions about people and situations that we describe as instinctive and for which, regrettably, we search for rational explanations. Yet this search is futile because no such explanations exist. A liking for someone on the same floor in your block of flats or feeling drawn to a woman before you have even spoken to her are things that cannot be fathomed by our computer brain. So, unable to rely upon its power to explain things, which has become our *raison d'être*, we instead use terms such as 'affinity', 'charm' or 'being easy to get on with'. This boils down to absolutely nothing at all; we would do better to hold our tongue and to sniff more sharply what is right in front of our noses.

This mystification is nowhere better disguised than in our sexual relationships since it is here that our sense of smell works to the greatest effect. Unfortunately, though, it is also here that our education and our culture have most blinded us to all these messages. I say 'blinded' intentionally, not only because it is the word that comes spontaneously to mind but because linguistic use allows it for describing loss of information. The word aptly reveals our old habit of disowning certain senses in favour of our 'supreme vision'.

I will not look in any greater detail here at the role smells play when we choose a sexual partner; I will expand on this topic later. For the time being, I want to give you two rather astonishing examples of this type of communication taken from the animal world. As interesting as these individual examples are, I am using them so that you sense what can happen among other species too.

Such illustrations are preferable to any theoretical demonstration and allow us to easily draw conclusions by noting what it is we still have in common with these animals, which have never felt ashamed about their sense of smell.

The bombyx silk moth's bewitching aerosol

The female of a certain type of silk moth, well known to specialists, is able to secrete the pheromone bombykol, a very simple chemical molecule that is of no interest whatsoever to any other species living in the same territory. In its usual concentration, man is not even aware of it. This harmless secretion will disperse in the atmosphere and over a radius of several miles set all the male setae (bristles) trembling. Once the male moth receives this smell message, you can see him go into real 'muscular activity overdrive', which shows that he is experiencing intense turmoil. Now all he wants to do is travel back up the air current that brought this message to him. To us, it may seem that flying back up a slight breeze, against the current, is an easy thing for a moth to do. In actual fact this represents an enormous feat, one that is remarkably similar to the salmon's migration when these famous oily fish battle upstream against the current and lose a good proportion of their body reserves doing so.

One of the features of this behaviour is that as he struggles determinedly against the wind, the male has not even seen the female who gave off the bombykol. He has no idea at all what is driving him to confront such adversity. He is not even aware that he is under the spell of a chemical message. He flies on, using up every last bit of energy, sustained by the smell of the bombykol which grows stronger and more concentrated the closer he gets to the female sending it out.

Moreover, he is never the only male to get caught up in this bewitching aerosol spray. Male moths, totally oblivious to what awaits them, come rushing from wherever the message has managed to spread. Moths are not blessed with consciousness but even if they were, they would probably still not know why and where they were rushing to in such a hurry.

Let's try the experiment anyway and for a brief moment bestow upon them our capabilities for highly sophisticated reasoning. They would then have no difficulty whatsoever in finding good reasons for this intense need for physical exertion. A large number of these males would talk about the need to exercise; for others it would be the desire to travel or explore. Lastly, I am certain that a lot of them would have no qualms about mentioning an idea as meaningless as a 'taste for action'.

I took the liberty of moving from moth to man without any transition, to illustrate how our refusal to accept this type of message, and many other equally natural ones, drives us to invent rational lies and alibis that collapse like a house of cards and are revealed as completely absurd once we know the mundane and simple truth.

Believing that he is flying just for his pleasure alone, our male moth is bound to reach his destination.

Once he gets to the end of his journey, along with hundreds of other male moths, he will find the female whose scent, carried along by the winds, was the natural trigger for a drive that is common to all species. However, if for a moment he still had the power of reasoning we lent him, the male would think that all this was the most amazing coincidence or good fortune.

This is only one step away from describing the encounter as predestined or talking about having feelings of premonition and the other balderdash we often hear being spoken by our species. However, I am too fond of white moths to foist our aberrations on them.

'It has been calculated that if a single female moth released all the bombykol she is carrying in one go, theoretically she could attract a billion males straightaway.' This is of course not what happens, as the species would have quickly died out, victim of the males' overpowering virility.

The fragrant world of rats

There can be no better example of olfactory communication than the male moth, literally put under a sexual spell by the smell of its female. However, it could be retorted that this little creature is only an insect and that we are way ahead of it on evolution's path.

To parry this objection, I have chosen rats, real mammals, to give us further insight into this type of communication.

Rats are one of the most cruel and most disturbing species on earth. Along with man, they share the dubious distinction of considering as enemies anyone who does not belong to their group and during fights with rivals they can kill without the slightest inhibition.

Rats live in large groups that usually develop from breeding within a single family, so all the members are related, and they live an extremely peaceful life with one another. The different mothers group together their litters in the same nest and do not seem to recognize their own young. There is no leader or hierarchy within this super-family.

Observation shows that everything radiates calm and there is never any fighting between the members of the clan. They hunt for food together and it is shared out fairly. There is not even any serious fighting to possess females; as there is total sexual promiscuity females do not belong to any male.

If we try to understand the underlying reason for such amazing harmony and pacifism we will discover – and this is what is of interest to us – that smell is what cements this society together. Rats in a group do not recognize each other individually; they cannot make out which rat is their mother or their brother or sister and certainly not which is their father. However, what they do instinctively know is that they all belong to the same group. They do not understand this; they smell it with their big snouts because within the same clan they are used to mixing their secretions by touching each other and by marking their territory with their urine and droppings.

They also mark clan members by urinating on one another and this permanent exchange sets up a super-scent cocktail within which they know themselves to be safe and are able to lead a quiet life.

This peaceful colony, permeated by its family scent, is inevitably thrown into disarray as soon as any unknown rat strays on to its territory. When this happens, what the rats can do to the intruder is more horrible than anything we might witness elsewhere among animals. The foreign rat may walk around for a few moments until he gets close enough for his unknown scent to be detected by one of the clan rats. This foreign scent acts like a very powerful signal which sets off a 'piercing cry' with a diabolical tonality that all the members of the clan join in with. Then, with their eyes bulging with excitement and their fur standing on end, all the rats pounce on the stranger and rip it to pieces in a particularly appalling act of carnage.

The best that can happen to this poor lost rat is that it dies of fright from nervous shock as has often been observed. If not, it will be literally torn apart alive, harried and bitten all over. 'It is rare to be able to read so clearly in an animal's expression despair and panicked fear and at the same time the certainty of inescapable and dreadful death.' The foreign rat is rooted to the spot in fear which prevents it from defending itself, whereas on any other occasion a cornered rat would be very aggressive and extremely dangerous.

To be absolutely sure that scent was causing this rapid detection, Irenäus Eibl-Eibesfeldt, the founder of human ethology, took a rat away from its family and washed it until its entire scent message had been removed. After this seemingly harmless shampoo, the rat was returned to its territory and it was immediately outlawed because it no longer had its protective scent. The rat only escaped a most horrible death because the scientist intervened to rescue it.

This same rat, smeared once again with a little earth and some bits taken from the group nest, quite quickly regained its family's scent and, even after a few weeks' absence, once placed back on the clan's territory was accepted without any hesitation.

So rats live in a world of scents where feeding, sexual relations, life and death depend on having a few more or a few less chemical molecules that their huge snout, this unsettling radar, can detect without the least possible error. Their other senses are also undoubtedly at work providing the rats with their share of information. However, it is scent that has taken over and like a tyrant largely dominates their communication.

Auditory communication among birds

Birds often communicate with one another through sound signals. Everyone knows the chirping, whistling, cheeping and cooing of our nightingales, chaffinches and pigeons.

All these sounds carry a message; chance plays no part here. Bird breeders and animal behaviour experts are well aware that the cockerel's cock-a-doodle-doo is laden with meaning for the chickens around him in the farmyard.

However, I have chosen the female turkey and her poults as they provide the most forceful illustration of this auditory communication.

Wolfgang and Margaret Schleidt, assistants to Professor Konrad Lorenz, were working with some turkeys that had been turned deaf for another completely different experiment. Apart from being deaf, the way these turkeys behaved socially and sexually was quite normal. So they were able to lay eggs and sit on them. 'However, once their chicks had hatched, the maternal behaviour of these females turned out to be disturbed to an absolutely catastrophic degree. They immediately turned on their young as soon they were born and pecked them to death.'

Having observed such aberrant behaviour, these researchers were led to postulate that for normal turkeys the only communication possible between mother and chicks had to be auditory.

A normal turkey, who has just sat on her eggs, watches a little fluffy chick emerge from its shell for the first time but does not yet understand that this chick is her own young. Like all turkeys, and especially while brooding, her hormones make her particularly aggressive towards anything that appears in her field of vision. So she attacks every moving object that comes close to her nest. She will react as ferociously with a hamster, a cat, a polecat and even her own poult.

However, when this turkey poult sees its mother descending on it, the chick instinctively lets out a cheep that is its species' particular sound and it is this little cry that straightaway defuses the mother's aggression and activates her maternal behaviour.

All of a sudden, the turkey responds to this cheeping with 'programmed' clucking and instead of bearing down on her chick she sets about mothering it.

To confirm this observation, you only have to show the mother turkey a stuffed turkey poult pulled along with a piece of nylon string and she will launch into a ferocious attack. A stuffed polecat will suffer the same fate. But if a small transistor is placed under its stomach playing a recording of a turkey poult's cheeping, oddly enough the female turkey will treat the stuffed polecat with all the signs of maternal behaviour. 'It is really quite something

to watch how this female turkey that was intent on peck-
ing the mute chick to death, now down on the ground
with the squeaking polecat baby, takes it under its wing
and utters maternal gobbling noises.'

These experiments are very informative and we can
learn much from them. They show us that female turkeys
do have maternal behaviour but that it is only activated
once they can hear their own poults' special cheeping. So
this is indeed typical non-verbal animal communication.

A little later on, we will see how a human mother reacts
more or less in the same way to her child's first reflex
smiles. This is very different to Elisabeth Badinter's
historical and cultural analysis of what is going on here.
The French historian argued in her book, *Mother Love:
Myth and Reality*, that the maternal instinct itself does
not exist.

Visual trigger signals

At last we have reached a sensory field where we have
nothing to envy other creatures. There are probably few
animals that have better visual acuity than us. What is
more, from childhood onwards, we are constantly learning
to improve our recognition of shapes and colours. Writing,
graphics, pictorial art, cinema, cartoons and television all
appeal to our system of perception, and nowadays they
impact on children at an ever younger age.

It is because we have become so familiar with what is
visual that I have chosen this area to explore the

difference between animal communication and human communication in greater detail.

This difference is at the very core of my argument which will eventually prove to you why and how men prefer 'women with curves'. So you see I have not strayed off-piste and am indeed keeping to this book's main theme.

MacLean's astounding discovery

I have a particular liking for Paul MacLean, the American neurobiologist who was responsible for the 'three brain theory' and the revelation I had after reading about it. I cannot help thinking that his discovery reaches a pinnacle, providing a way of ordering the findings of many scientists and scholars who are patiently working away in their respective fields.

MacLean specialized in the nervous system; he spent much of his life dissecting skulls and investigating animal and human brains with a keen sense of observation.

A nervous system is an organ that allows its owner to gather all the information provided by the surrounding world and to activate behaviour that best promotes survival and reproduction. It is the orchestra's conductor, and without it we would be nothing more than simple green plants.

MacLean realized, as does any biologist, that the higher up we go in the animal kingdom, the larger and more complex brains become and the better able they are to perform. However, while studying these different brains he had his first revelation.

He noticed that instead of innovating and inventing a completely new brain for each great step up, nature made do and kept the old brain, adding to it a new layer or, rather, a new tier. This enabled the creatures that were given this new tier to aspire to much improved performance. But in doing so – and here is what is so very interesting about this discovery – the old brain continued to exist and to work in the same way as before. We human beings come at the very end of the nervous system's evolution and therefore beneath our skull we possess all the superimposed brains that came into being before us.

1. Buried very deep down, we therefore have a first, primitive brain that nature had already given to the reptiles. What we are able to do with this brain, the dinosaurs already did hundreds of millions of years before us and lizards do today.

In this area is found what drives us to live and reproduce. If we suddenly had the preposterous idea of dying, resistance to this idea would come from this well-hidden, small grey mass. This is our *raison d'être* in its primitive stage.

If the French philosopher, Albert Camus, had been able to imagine this brain, perhaps he would not have philosophized as he did about the absurdity of life. If we go to enormous lengths to eat and drink, if we fight with self-confidence or if we are afraid, again it is in this part of the brain that everything is organized and triggered.

And if some incomprehensible force alerts us that we are in the presence of a female, again it is down to this part of our brain. The smell, the curves, the texture of breasts or hips, the impact of a woman requesting protection, the reaction sparked by a pupil dilating, the agitation felt by a mother seeing her child smile for the first time; the irrepressible need to humble oneself before an important person, our sense of hierarchy and the absurd respect shown to a dominant figure are all signals that lizards, birds, wolves and men react to in the same way, while, of course, taking account of each species' individual traits.

At this level, everything is triggered with absolute total unconsciousness. There is a stimulation that triggers something and then there is a reaction. This is how the lizard, a cold-blooded animal, still lives today.

2. On to this old reptilian brain, a second layer has been added, a bit like having a second scoop of ice cream piled on top of the first one in a cone.

With this new brain, which appeared along with the mammals, we now reach the domain of emotions. And what we do with them, a small rodent like the beaver was already doing tens of thousands of years before us.

From now on, every message that reaches us not only sparks an effective response but it also becomes coloured by and enriched with emotion.

However, and this detail is extremely important, these emotions are not yet conscious. Here again we are dealing with reactions adapted to survival. Faced with an enemy, our heart starts beating quickly, our hair stands on end, our eyes dilate and the blood rises to our face. All these changes will help in the fight that is going to ensue.

This is what happens when performers go on stage. The stage fright they experience is simply the interior turmoil that is preparing them to go into battle. If performers tremble this is because they are being swamped with huge energy reserves they cannot use. The lizard never trembles, its heart is quiet. The rat or the wolf shakes with emotion without being the least bit aware of it. Only man is aware of his joys and his terrors.

It is here in this brain that our feelings and emotions linked to maternal dependency, and later to love, take shape. Pangs of anguish, a lump in the throat, sweaty hands, burning desires, butterflies in the stomach, feeling knocked sideways, being fiery-tempered, having a dry mouth, a voice going hoarse, stomach pangs, fainting from fear or joy, tears, laughter – it is the second brain that makes all these things happen. But it is also here that we store away our memories of emotional experiences. When Proust is transported back to his childhood by tasting a madeleine cake, or when an adult is still frightened of the dark or refuses to swim, it is because a very intense emotional trace of these fears or bad experiences has been left behind in this little part of the brain.

Dreaming, too, comes with a violent emotional charge that can explode into our nightmares just as it does into those of our cats and dogs. And many drugs that today are known as 'tranquillizers' directly tap into the anxiety that colours our behaviour.

Finally, coming back to what is of specific interest to us: women's curves, perceived visually and by touch, smell and many other stimulations of a sexual nature, trigger in us emotions that we are incapable of controlling.

3. Lastly, the third brain or the neo-cortex is like a coat that goes on top of everything. It is the nervous system's final acquisition. In cats and dogs it is modest; it has expanded in monkeys and reaches its culmination in man. This is the brain of reasoning, language, reading and writing, logic and mathematics.

Father of invention, mother of abstract thought, it is the purveyor of ideas and culture.

Nevertheless, however rich it may be, it is still only a computer, albeit of astonishing complexity. In itself it has no warmth and most importantly no decision-making power, and here lies the misunderstanding with the most complications humankind will ever know.

The problem with these three brains arises from the fact that although they are housed under the same roof they speak three different languages.

The first brain perceives messages that are directed at the instincts and it responds with appropriate decisions. This brain decides about everything relating to survival, in other words everything that gives meaning to our existence. If you are trying to work out what makes you chase after women, fortune and power, don't go looking – it all takes place here above your eyebrows.

The second brain gives our behaviour warmth and colour; it has a knack for causing a stir. It is this brain that was responsible for the glaringly obvious difference between two great tennis heroes, Bjorn Borg and John McEnroe. The first, an ice-cool Viking, enigmatic but effective, may have perhaps looked like some other-worldly being but he played as a lizard would, which is why he was so impressive. The second, a cantankerous Irish-American, would shake, grind his teeth, lose his temper and fly into a rage. His behaviour was influenced by his second brain.

The third brain, the one to which we ascribe all our humanity, decides nothing; it has no warmth but it does want to explain everything. Even if it does manage terribly well to understand what is happening around us, it is completely hopeless when it comes to anything that the two other brains deal with, and they deal with what really matters. And it is here that one of the tragedies of our human nature arises – this third brain abuses its power. Accustomed to analyzing, unravelling and working everything out, it gets nowhere fast when faced with things it does not comprehend. It searches and eventually finds reasons for our behaviour, decisions and emotions. It can at times hit the nail on the head but more often than not this third brain gets it wrong and invents false reasons to justify impulses that came from another place.

To sum up this three-brain theory and get straight back to our topic, I am claiming that a male of our species, standing in front of his female, will take in the shape of her breasts, the contours of her eyes and lips, the triangle of her pubic hair made conspicuous by a completely hairless body, and the characteristic, distinct roundness of her hips and thighs. He will breathe in the smell from her skin, her neck and armpits, and through direct contact he will feel the texture and elastic fullness of her bosom and behind.

Thanks to his sense organs, he is aware of all these sensations and the messages will reach all three brains at the same time. The first responds with a sexual urge that will drive him to possess this body. The second sparks a sexual emotion that will disrupt his circulatory and respiratory rhythms, speed up his heart rate and make it easier for him to accomplish the task he is about to undertake. However, at the same time, these messages also flood his third brain where consciousness holds sway, totally unfamiliar with the language of our emotions and instincts which are nevertheless so necessary for survival.

There, these messages will confront the cultural archetypes predominant in the society in which the man lives. And if by misfortune current trends favour an absence of shape and smell, a conflict will arise between the primitive brain and the new one, a conflict between the wild one and the computer one, between the conscious and the subconscious, which since Freud's work we all know results either in neurosis or sublimation. However, we will look at this in greater detail later on, along with ways of finding a remedy for this conflict by trying to harmonize the cultural and the natural.

For the time being, we still need to absorb a little more information about the possibilities of animal communication so that no doubt remains whatsoever about how it works and what it can trigger in us.

This time, the two examples I have chosen to illustrate visual trigger signals come from the world of fish.

The stickleback and the Siamese fighting fish are two amazing fish whose sexuality is a model of beauty and perfection.

These two fish are perhaps the most aggressive in the whole aquatic world. And if scaled up to size, their violence is more intense than that of the most destructive sharks.

As we will see, the sexual act of these fish is triggered, controlled and guided throughout by visual signals based on colour, shape and expressive movements. Interestingly, these two terrors of the aquarium are model fathers. They build their nests themselves and chase their females away so that they can look after the eggs and the young on their own.

The stickleback's great colour display

The stickleback is a small freshwater fish that lives in a shoal. When the breeding season comes round, the male fish takes himself off and seeks out his territory. He will opt for an area where the ground is soft and where he can easily build his nest.

Once he has found his spot, his exterior changes colour

and grows brighter. He needs this to happen as he has to look impressive and keep away other male fish from his shoal, which are also trying to build their nest.

If, by mistake, another male fish appears and tries to enter the stickleback's territory, his colours flare up and his body takes on a 'threatening posture'. These signals indicate his emotional state and show that he is feeling belligerent. Usually the intruder reacts by escaping or avoiding him and that is as far as things go.

However, if the new male fish insists on trespassing, then there is a fight. Sticklebacks attack without any warning and with such intensity that it is impossible to follow the fight with the naked eye. Almost always it is the male with nothing to defend who comes off worst and who by instinct, sensing the greater aggressiveness, flees before his sides get ripped open.

After several battles, the male fish's territory is no longer contested and he can then begin building his nest. He does this instinctively, without any instruction, by digging into the ground to make a little narrow tunnel where the eggs will be laid.

Once his nest is finished, the next phase starts, which is of most interest to us – the courtship display with its wonderful ballet and explosion of colours and shapes, when the male and female fish communicate solely through visual trigger signals. And this communication, which takes place thanks to the old instinctive brain, results in the eggs being fertilized.

So once his nest is complete, the male's colours start to

grow bright. His back turns an iridescent aquamarine colour, his eyes become a striking emerald and his stomach and sides in particular gleam bright red.

Meanwhile, the female fish, which are maturing their eggs, swim around together and approach the male fishes' territory.

The first visual signal that acts as a trigger comes from the female and in particular from her 'bloated stomach'. This shape is particularly expressive when the female is ready to lay her eggs and it leads the male to exhibit very specific parading and courtship behaviour.

The male performs a 'zigzag' dance, going back and forth many times; he pretends to go away only to suddenly return with his mouth wide open. This zigzag dance, along with the red stomach, is a further sexual stimulant and it attracts the female so powerfully that she makes straight for the male. By playing this game, the male gradually manages to manoeuvre her over towards his nest. Once they reach the entrance to the tunnel he has so carefully built, he makes as if he is going inside and then he moves away. This gesture is also a signal that impels the female to do likewise and after several attempts, she goes right inside the nest and leaves only her head and tail sticking out.

The male then places its face at the bottom of the female's tail and starts trembling violently. This tactile message is crucial for what happens next because without it everything would just stop. The vibrations and rubbing automatically induce the female to lay her eggs. Once the female has left the nest, the male enters after her and now a chemical or olfactory signal from the liquid in which the eggs have been laid gets to work and this smell acts like a reflex, inducing the male to release his sperm and fertilize the eggs.

The male quickly comes out of the nest and chases the female off his territory. Since releasing his semen has satisfied his sexual instinct and his excitement at seeing the bloated female abdomen has subsided, he now reverts to being aggressive. At this moment, he no longer has any memory or any awareness of what has just taken place and he will violently attack anything that could pose a threat to his fertilized eggs.

This example is of interest to us because it provides us with new signals that we are unaware of, and for the first time we see how swelling and plenitude in a certain part of the body can act as a triggering signal. A flat abdomen leaves the male indifferent; the sexual courtship display is stimulated and triggered by the female's swelling with its full and substantial curve.

The male's aphrodisiac red colour is also something new for us. And it is curious to note that this coloured surface occurs in just the same way in another very distant species, the robin redbreast. The male bird's red throat and breast trigger the same sexual attraction.

The female robin usually has a grey-coloured breast. However, if her breast feathers are painted red, you will see other female birds submit to her in an almost sexual way as they react to the signal with no awareness whatsoever that they are being hoodwinked.

The Siamese fighting fish, the male chauvinist of the rivers

Here too is a small freshwater fish but this one has an extremely belligerent nature. I will not go over the nest-building and egg-fertilization details again. This example will provide us with one new signal we are unaware of, and yet it is vitally important as it paves the way to a sexuality that leads us to man.

Pay careful attention to this signal as it appears for the first time in fish and will be found all along the animal evolutionary path. Man still reacts to this mysterious trigger without even realizing it.

Unlike the stickleback, the fighting fish is not an animal that proudly announces its gender through its colours. There is no bright red or emerald green here; a few luminous markings and some iridescent streaks on the fins at the very most. And because of this, animal behaviour experts puzzled for a long time over how the male of the species recognized his female.

Béatrice Oehlert, one of Konrad Lorenz's students, studied these fighting fish over a long period. By dint of her patience, she eventually discovered the mysterious signal they give out.

Whenever he surprises a fish of his species trespassing on his territory the male fighting fish, terror of the waters, does not immediately know the gender of the stranger. Only his aggressiveness drives him towards the interloper. Confronting the other fish, he adopts 'the domination attitude', when the creature vaunts itself and tries to present itself in as terrifying a mien as possible. 'It displays its fins in such a spectacular, sudden and intense way that you can almost hear the rustle of a parasol suddenly opening.'

This posture is a signal that radiates strength and self-confidence. If the fighting fish is dealing with another male, the second male will respond with the same show of power. He responds to the threat with a counter-threat and the chances are that a fight will soon get underway which more often than not results in the death of one of the combatants.

If the other fish is a female who is ready to mate, she will respond with an attitude and behaviour that immediately identify her gender. Instead of swaggering like a male fish, she quickly submits by folding away her fins and making herself look as vulnerable as possible. As well as this, she approaches the male gently, timidly and without any brusqueness.

What can be detected in all these movements is a mixture of attraction and fright that has great expressive value and is called 'prudery behaviour'.

Konrad Lorenz cleverly sums up what is going on by saying that for the male there is no compromise between fear and sexuality. If the female inspires any fear in him, his sexuality is totally obliterated. On the other hand, the female who respects 'her partner so little that his aggressiveness is not completely eliminated is incapable of responding sexually to him'.

So here we have the first appearance of the fundamental concept that haunts animal sexuality: power, arrogance and impetuousness are characteristics associated with male sexuality. This is what we in our species call virility.

Gentleness, charm and vulnerability are associated with female sexuality. We tend to name this femininity.

In the way they manifest themselves, virility and femininity represent two completely opposed poles of behaviour. This is the north and the south of sexuality. Any attempt to try to bring them closer together or tone down their antagonism is a sure-fire way of eroding their attractive forces and producing impotency and frigidity.

2. Non-verbal communication in man

We have just quickly surveyed the amazing world of animal communication. We will go no further now in this book, apart from looking at the legacy animals have passed on to us, which, without us being aware of it, has probably made it possible for us to still be here today.

Before our species appeared on earth, everything that was alive used to communicate solely by exchanging sensory signals, which meant that instincts were totally responsible for ensuring life and reproduction.

Man arrived and the miracle came about that allowed us to acquire a second language, conscious speech.

This gift, which opens up perspectives that today we still only in part glimpse, did not, however, in any way suppress the means of communication that we shared with the rest of the living world. Far from it, and nature, nonetheless generous, had foreseen our ingratitude and had laid down for good the fundamental ground rules for our existence and survival in the dark regions of our unconscious.

Nobody would dispute that speech has enabled humankind to take giant leaps in the ways it can express itself. Yet the richness and autonomy of this language are such that it has entirely taken over our field of consciousness. It has relegated our primitive communication, and with it the basic realities of human nature, to a completely inaccessible subconscious. This leads to the surprising paradox that we may well talk just for the pure pleasure of listening to ourselves, or, what is worse, as a way of disguising our genuine, instinctive motivations or finding an alibi for them.

The sexual arena is the one that offers our species its greatest guarantee of continuity. Leaving aside test-tube babies, we have not yet found a better way of reproducing ourselves.

Given the importance of what is at stake, our instincts and our animal communication, which in most other areas have lost ground, have survived well here. Freud was one of the first to highlight the importance of the hidden and subconscious role our libido plays.

Despite the fuss caused by this theory which seemed so scandalous at the time, now nobody would still deny that we have inside us a powerful sex drive.

What is less acknowledged, and what to some extent this book is all about, is that this sexual instinct which comes from our animal side requires a whole range of trigger signals to be able to express itself and find something to focus on. One of these signals, the curve of hips, pelvis and thighs, the tactile firmness of their texture, the fullness of breasts: in a nutshell women's curves, these are typical, but unfortunately subconscious, triggers for our sexual instinct.

Discredited for a long time by absurd fashions and culture, these magnetic signals collide with a cultural screen and the shock of them being rejected impacts on the harmony of our behaviour, subconsciously throwing us into disarray.

I will deal with this in the following chapters. To finish with the subject here, I would like to give two brief examples of primitive communication in man. To be quite sure that we can completely discount the role language plays, I have deliberately chosen infants before they are able to speak, and blind people for whom light, shapes and colours have forever vanished.

The natural smile: a signal that triggers maternal instinct

At birth, the human infant is totally blind. After maturing over a few weeks a baby is able to see properly.

The neuro-psychoanalyst, René Spitz, famous for his work on emotional behaviour in infants, was the first to discover that smiling is a natural reflex that appears in the seventh week after birth. Before, it was thought that this exclusively human expression was acquired and that we developed it through contact with our parents and by imitating them.

To trigger this reflex, all you have to do is place a human face in front of the baby, ideally one metre away. The infant always reacts in the same way, whatever the gender, age or race of the face.

Intrigued by his discovery, Spitz wanted to learn more about which parts of the face were triggering this reflex. He patiently carried out his research on a great number of children and observed that if the face was in profile the baby's smile would disappear. He concluded from this that both eyes were indispensable. To confirm this and to find out more about what triggers smiling he used the decoy techniques that the psychoanalyst Tinbergen had promoted. So he made some masks, which always had a single feature of the human face missing, and he came to the conclusion that the absolute minimum to elicit this reflex smile was the two eyes, the eyebrows and the nose.

The mouth, the hairline and ears were not essential. So this meant there actually was a specific configuration for which we are already programmed before birth. Eibl-Eibesfeldt, an expert in the field of human behaviour, confirmed this theory in an unusual way by working with children who were deaf, dumb and blind from birth. Unfortunately, such children are of course unable to learn anything visually.

The films of his work are moving and with them he was able to prove that smiling is indeed an untaught, natural reflex. Despite there being no natural trigger for these children, they do start to smile for reasons that are well known in behavioural biology. When over a certain period a natural reflex has not been triggered, it is bound to express itself through responding to other parallel stimulations.

Infants thus afflicted, who will never be able to gaze upon a human face, end up smiling if their neck or body is gently caressed. These same infants, who have no means of imitating others, do far more than smile. Once they are irritated by some unpleasant stimulation and they become angry, they then cry, stamp their feet, clench their fists and screw up their faces. In doing so they are showing us that all such motor movements and expressions are innate and there is absolutely no need for them to be learnt.

To come back to smiling, let us take a look at how it works as a trigger for any sort of communication. Nature would never create a pattern of motor movement as complex as this without good reason. A smile has a target; it is meant to be seen by the person who is there looking at the infant, as soon as it is seven weeks old. And this person is almost always the mother. The child's smiling face triggers inside her protective behaviour and tender feelings that will be the start of a deep, life-long bond.

The maternal instinct is there in women, but like any instinct it needs to be triggered and then kept going. The child's unconscious, reflex smiling is one of these triggers and there may well be many others too. The crying and clumsy gestures, the rounded and disproportionately large size of the infant's head and in particular its eyes and forehead are all signals sent out by the child that experts today are trying to decipher. It is still too early to be able to say for sure that they are also triggers, but already there are many convincing presumptions that favour this hypothesis.

Be that as it may, there is plenty of concrete evidence about smiling and it is most definitely part of our instinctive communication. After the seventh month, it is no longer simply a reflex action and the infant will smile much more selectively. The infant will no longer react to any face but will now respond primarily to its mother's face, then to its father's face, then the faces of those people close to it and all the familiar faces that it loves. Later on, once the child has reached full maturity, smiling will take on its full human function which is to attract a positive response from the people we encounter by miraculously defusing any aggression. In a nutshell, one smile elicits another smile.

How infants communicate through smell

A French researcher, Hubert Montagner, carried out a series of experiments with very young children in nurseries which seem to prove that their mother's smell is a subconscious signal they recognize and which helps them with their emotional and social interactions.

In an initial experiment, all the mothers of the children in the nursery were asked to wear a T-shirt next to their skin for three days and three nights without taking it off. Then all the children were left with T-shirts on a table in front of them, their mother's one included, and they were asked to pick one out. It was observed that most of the children who were happy to choose a T-shirt took their mother's garment.

In the second experiment, a certain number of children were selected from among those who had already chosen their mother's T-shirt and it was given back to them. These children tended to keep the T-shirt with them. Their interaction was then filmed and analyzed by psychologists. They came to the definite conclusion that these children were less aggressive than usual. In their class, they were the ones who most actively sought out exchanges, games and communication with the other infants. Simply having the smell of their mother with them, preserved in the object they were holding, was enough to make them more sociable and more communicative.

Both experiments prove unequivocally that the infant recognizes its mother's smell when she is not there and that this comforting scent modifies the child's behaviour from a distance.

The curious world of the blind

For anyone who has an interest in non-verbal communication in man, observing people who are blind provides a wealth of information that is a challenge to interpret. Eibl-Eibesfeldt was able to watch and film children who were blind and deaf from birth. Just by using smell, these children can work out whether a person is someone they know or a complete stranger. Although all the people with whom they come into contact try to be nice to them and make them feel safe, the children will turn away from someone they do not know and kick out in their direction.

Most adult blind people, despite their serious impairment, manage to live in society. Often they even work and are able to move around big cities.

When they find themselves with people they do not know, they very quickly succeed in gathering a mass of information that they are incredibly clever at synthesizing. I personally knew someone who had been a doctor before losing his sight during the Franco-Algerian war. Twelve years later he was a top masseur. When he met someone new, he had no trouble in determining their age or emotional state from the timbre of their voice or their smell.

One day I took along a young relative of mine who lived in the provinces as she was suffering from a pain in her shoulder. After only saying hello to her, he took me to one side and said: 'She is a terribly pretty young girl, why don't you tell her to dress a bit more fashionably? She needs to get out more; her shyness is getting her down.'

Apart from the fact that he was absolutely right, this anecdote serves no other purpose of course than to demonstrate the extent to which blind people rely on information that we do not even deign to absorb.

Conclusion

Some of you are perhaps thinking that I have taken a rather long detour to arrive at the truth that the whole living world communicates thanks to sensory messages and by instinct.

Apart from the magical beauty of the examples we have looked at, this detour was essential to make what we are going to look at next absolutely crystal clear.

Given that scientific experiments on man are of course impossible, I needed some indirect evidence. My argument turned into a speech for the defence and to convince you I had to rely upon overwhelming testimony from animals. So they came to the witness box and, without any collusion between them, they all gave you – the jury – the same statement.

Right throughout the animal kingdom we find a male sex and a female sex that function like a magnet's negative and positive poles. These two poles are connected by a force which is the sex drive. This drive is not blind and each species has its own sexual signals that it sends out and receives.

From all these testimonies, the fundamental observation is that as it moves up from one level to the next nature does not go in for much innovation; a little more smell for rats, some more of the visual with fish, and for birds a bit more of the acoustic. However, most communication still takes place through sensory signals.

I needed to make you sense the full weight of this evidence because we know that, since Darwin, humankind can no longer claim to have supernatural origins.

Whether we like it or not, we are the direct descendants of all these witnesses so we cannot disclaim them. At

the very most we can point out that since our consciousness came on the scene it has to some extent enabled us
to detach ourselves from our instincts. However, culture
has crept into the void, and by singing its sirens' song it
leads our minds astray by making them think that they
can act with total free will.

We can exploit and reign over the rest of the living
world; we can leave our footsteps on uninhabited planets
and harness the atom. Yet we are today still unable to do
anything to change the fact that we are biologically identical to our Cro-Magnon ancestors and share with them
the same urges and drives as well as that bit of instinct
we still need to reproduce ourselves and survive.

Acknowledging the sexual drive in us has been the
fruit of a bitter struggle and for this to happen it needed
the genius and stubbornness of someone like Sigmund
Freud, who for a long time was exposed to public condem-
nation and mockery, levelled at him by obscurantists of
all shades of opinion.

Nowadays, surely the way has been paved for us to
state that if we have a sexual instinct then we are bound
to have the signals that trigger it as well? It might appear
obvious to say that without these signals we would have
no valid reason for preferring a woman to a wardrobe or
an attractive-looking rocking chair!

And yet I realize that accepting such obvious ideas
does not always mean that these trigger signals receive
recognition. A rather large number of otherwise intelligent people have difficulty acknowledging that apart

from their breastfeeding function, women's breasts might have a role to play as a sexual trigger.

Likewise they are unable to accept that if there was no point in the typical shapeliness of women's hips and thighs, we would have to despair about nature and believe that she creates quite randomly and without any purpose.

Nor can they accept that if women lost their hair and men kept theirs, this was not simply the result of tossing a coin.

And they have trouble admitting that if we have inherited personal odours as varied as our fingerprints, then this was not just to give us the pleasure of inventing and using anonymous, chemical deodorants.

For them, to affirm the contrary is to pay homage instead to nature, and, to paraphrase Einstein, 'nature cannot play dice with the universe'.

To call upon Freud and Einstein to make us recognize that all these messages have a meaning and that they trigger in us a temptation to preserve our species is perhaps going a bit far. However, if these signals were not real, the odds are that these two great men would themselves never have existed.

3. Femininity, a biological cocktail

What makes a naïve person naïve is that they ask questions with disarming simplicity, questions that we cannot always answer. Children and scientists are naturally inclined to ask such simple questions since they both have the same overpowering need to understand the world around them.

'What is a woman?'

This question is as simple as it is embarrassing because there is no satisfactory answer. In its naïvety, the child will tell us that a woman is not a man. After much thought, the perplexed scientist will feel that he cannot do any better.

This paradox boils down to the fact that the existence of the sexes is not a convention that we have chosen and is something that was imposed on the living world well before we appeared on the scene. So one sex in isolation means absolutely nothing in itself and it can only be defined with reference to the other sex.

To recognize a woman, a man has no need whatsoever to reason, he feels it instinctively. By this I mean that if he needed to use his intelligence to consciously work out this 'diagnosis' he would spend much of his time deciding about the women he might come across during his day.

So once again it is our old brain that decides in a split second, in an almost reflex manner, by ascertaining certain clear, simple signals that provide confirmation without any need for argument or proof.

Here is another striking example of the mirage, when our consciousness deludes itself about its role by usurping the fruit of purely instinctive knowledge and without even realizing it.

Animals did not wait around for us to be able to recognize each other, and they don't need much: a mere smell, the movement of a fin or a tail, a strong colour and all aggression disappears as the temptation to copulate takes hold.

As surprising as this might appear to you, we have absolutely no superiority over them in this area. We are reduced just like any old fish to responding in a binary fashion to certain signs we recognize. In a split second it will be 'yes' or 'no'. During this time, our conscious reasoning will take over and weigh up the pros and cons. However, what it does not realize is that our choice has already been long made and that we are no longer looking at things in quite the same way now that magnetic fields loaded with energy are crisscrossing, now that images are passing before our eyes conveying softness, charm and roundness, now that our nostrils are unconsciously dilating as we pick up a few intimate fragrances and our voice becomes laden with emotion and the slightest accidental brushing of skin is likely to fire us with desire.

So our animal communication is working at full stretch; while our computer brain is still struggling and sputtering away.

I am convinced that you will not be taking this description seriously and that you will think I am trying to spice things up by injecting a little humour. And yet this is what actually happens. Certainly, since our neurones get to work very rapidly, decisions are made in a trice. But what it is important to understand is that with this sort of knowledge, our instincts are far more rapid and above all far more reliable than our intellect.

The messages that come from women contain the ingredients for a cocktail that we tend to call 'femininity'. Each female of our species naturally possesses all the elements of this combination but what differentiates each woman, and therefore each combination, will be not only the quality of each ingredient but most importantly their proportion in the final combination. We are now entering the area of different types and the even narrower area of personality. This is the miracle of our own private predilections and our everyday attractions.

Let me explain myself. How many times have I heard the standard question: 'And what type of woman do *you* prefer?'

More often than not what this question is really getting at is: 'Do you have a preference for blondes or brunettes, for athletic women or delicate sophisticates, for sexy or intellectual women?'

And here again we come up against the word 'prefer' and we are still dealing with the same mystification. I believe I can reply that we actually have no choice. We are programmed to react to a particular type of combination.

When we talk about blondes, we do not just mean a hair colour. As a rule, a blonde has a very particular skin texture, smell and eye colour which all make up a specific structural whole. If we believe what biologists tell us, it is smell and skin texture that determine everything. However, if we had to go for one common denominator that at the very last moment clinches the decision, I would give the prize to curves – which is the reason why I wrote this book. The roundness and curviness that we currently frown upon are perhaps the most genuine signs of femininity and the ones that best define the difference between the sexes.

We are entering a period when at last serious people, rigorous scientists, are busy finding out who we really are. We are confronted with practically virgin territory and it will take some patience to clear this ground. But what surprising discoveries we have in store!

While we await this day, as an initial analysis, we should now list all the signals we can be certain about and that act upon us, poor men, bewitching us and leading us to where nature always intended us to go.

So, to be more specific, what are the elements that distinguish men from women? I am going to take a look at them and you may rest assured that combined together they are the most reliable way of defining womanhood today.

Pay careful attention as we track them down. If you are a male reader, ask yourself where your preferences lie. And if you are a woman, you will definitely be surprised to see how many elements you rate highly and how many you reject. The discrimination that lies behind your choices is based on essentially cultural reasons. And you have a great excuse for this. These signals you send out are not aimed at you and you are not at all programmed to respond to them. Which is probably the reason why you sometimes go along with society's meaningless dictates, and why, with regard to what concerns us, you shun with such ingratitude the very curves that have done so much for you.

Size

Statistically, it is accepted that women are smaller than men. There is a 10 per cent difference at least, regardless of race. To give a typical example, the equivalent of a man who is five foot nine inches (one metre eighty centimetres) tall, is a woman five foot four inches (one metre sixty-five centimetres) tall. Of course these are just average size differences and it is quite possible to come across very tall women and very small men. So in itself there is nothing decisive about this characteristic and its role as a sexual trigger is not important. It is an extra element and there is no known culture where men systematically seek out women taller than themselves.

So to sum up about size, we will posit an axiom which is bound to surprise our teenagers, who dream of living on tiptoe: all cultures being equal, a large woman is less feminine than a standard-sized one.

Body hair

Women have hair follicles distributed all over their bodies. However, apart from a few special areas, their body hair has vanished and remains only as a sort of fine, almost invisible down. In the next chapter we will see why women's hair has disappeared whereas all other female primates have kept theirs.

Men feel a real inhibition when confronted with female body hair. They put up with it, with little enthusiasm, on legs and arms but once it turns into a beard or covers breasts they experience real aversion. We can conclude that lack of hair on the face and bust is a typical sign of femininity. After the menopause and due to hormonal changes, this sign becomes less marked.

However, the tuft of pubic hair is an extremely feminine characteristic. A triangular shape with the apex seemingly pointing in the direction of the genitals, the edges are clearly delimited, and, as we will see later on, perform the role of a little-known but highly effective visual trigger.

Men do not have a triangle, but rather a diamond shape that goes up to the belly button and gets lost in the rest of their stomach hair. Asian women, and Japanese women in particular, generally have very little hair and many of them have a very inconspicuous pubic triangle. A few years ago I read reports from a plastic surgery conference held in Japan and, to my great surprise, discovered that there are Japanese plastic surgeons specializing in pubic hair transplants. That such a procedure is being carried out would lead us to believe that there is a demand to supplement or replace something that is missing.

Underarm hair is an apparently paradoxical exception and, although part of women's hair, it plays no role as a visual trigger. Generally, men are not bothered about it either way, but underarm hair plays a fundamental role in sexual relations for both men and women as smells get trapped in it. This is crucially important and in the next chapter we will see why and how.

Breasts

Whatever the culture or race, the female bust plays a role of paramount importance in differentiating the sexes. The curve and the fullness of breasts vary with age, ethnicity and the individual woman. Influenced by the folliculin hormone, breasts feel more swollen during the final part of the menstrual cycle.

Breasts may double or triple in size during pregnancy and a network of bluish veins may become visible.

Nipples, which men also have, are definitely more protuberant in women. The areola around the nipple is much wider and has more pigment. By signalling femininity, breasts play a crucial role as a sexual trigger. We will see how, and most importantly why, only human females have had the privilege of being able to retain them when not lactating.

Face

The female face of our species is so familiar to us that we would have great difficulty in actually listing what makes it specifically feminine.

Try this out on yourself or on the people you know well and you will be embarrassed by your inability to analyze those signs that allow you nonetheless to sense, in a split second, whether or not you are looking at a female face.

If you had to consciously analyze these signs, the odds are that you would not manage it and that your partner would have lost all patience before you had worked out their gender.

So we have to resign ourselves to accepting that innate factors help us which are just as much reflexes as the reflex actions that make us jump at a sudden loud noise.

The same sort of mechanism comes into play once you have to guess the age of a human face. Unconsciously and by instinct, with one look you absorb the small details and, as if by magic, they turn into a ballpark number. You would be terribly hard put to quickly give the reasons for your estimate. And here lies a mystery that computers or brain function experts are far from solving.

But let us return to the female face, and see what it tells us about femininity.

The eyes and the way they look

The eyes and the way they look probably convey the main message.

I have never read anything in any scientific publication that deals with this subject. Perhaps it is time we thought about it. The only known element refers to the angles at which the eyes open. As a rule, a woman's eyes are more open than a man's and the smile around the eyes more accentuated. I myself know no more and to those of you who are curious, I will entrust the task of observing yourselves.

However, there is something quite astounding in the female eye that was discovered by the eminent American psychologist, Eckhard Hess, a professor in Chicago. What he found made him more famous than all his other work; he devoted ten years of his life to it and he published a scientific bestseller about it. This exciting discovery, which I am dying to reveal to you here, will however have to wait until the next chapter because it relates to female biological sexuality in the same way as curves, which is what my argument will ultimately demonstrate.

Facial structure

The arch of the eyebrows, cheekbones and nose are three bony elements surrounding the eyes that make up the contours of the face. In women, they are markedly less distinct, less protruding and less heavy than in men. It is easy to understand why because at the time when the human face was differentiating itself from ape species, man was a hunter and so his eyes were his greatest asset. It was therefore very useful for him to retain this protective bone structure. Woman, busy with home and offspring, had less need for them, so the contours of her face could soften, making the upper part of her head look delicate, vulnerable and softer, adding to her charm.

Likewise, the angle of her jaw is less obvious and less square.

And to add the final decisive touch, her whole bone structure is covered in a slightly fleshy top layer, enveloping her in softness and conveying a message of peace.

Hair, eyelashes and eyebrows

One of the main ingredients of womanhood is a head of hair. This is perhaps, paradoxically, the most immediately recognizable sexual element and a man with long hair is difficult to identify from behind.

And yet, hair can be cut and its length varies from one historical period to the next. So what conclusions should we draw?

One thing is certain: folliculin, the feminizing hormone par excellence, protects and strengthens hair while male hormones slowly destroy it. So, as a rule, women have a thicker, more abundant head of hair without a receding hairline.

It is highly likely that primitive man had to have shorter hair. A professional hunter, he could not for a moment allow himself to lose his prey from sight, even for the sake of his most beautiful locks. Had Bjorn Borg been deprived of his famous headbands at the height of his fame, he would no doubt have chopped his locks off to ensure that he could play at his very best.

When all is said and done, having long hair is an obvious message of femininity yet we have to acknowledge that this sign, so easy to modify, can change with fashions and cultural influences.

If the 1960s saw a fashion for men sporting long hair this has tended to die out, and as for basic archetypes you can still find pigtails in girls' boarding schools and flat-top haircuts in the officers' mess.

Eyelashes have a dual function. They protect the eyes from a whole array of harmful particles in the air and they bestow a mellowing softness. Women understand this well and since olden times have been darkening and curling their lashes. Lashes are the only hair that is at least as thick in women as in men. In his cartoons, Walt Disney was the first to caricature femininity when he added disproportionately large lashes to the eyes of his mice.

Lastly, female eyebrows are nowhere near as thick as their male equivalents. Again they have a dual function. They act as a 'gutter', diverting away any sweat that forms as beads on the forehead, and when both eyebrows are knitted together they form a sign across the face that identifies a man. Well aware just how brutal this signal can look, women often try to tone it down by plucking their brows.

The shoulder-to-hips ratio

For Konrad Lorenz, the father of ethology, this character-istic is one of the main triggering signs of womanhood.

'The contrast in men and women between the width of the hips and the width of the shoulders, the distribution of hairy areas and the shape of the female bust are specific indicators of sexual power that instinct knows, but not the head,' as Schopenhauer said.

Excessively large shoulders do not seem to sit well with femininity as their appearance alone is a sign of domi-nance and power. There are few armies anywhere that would think twice about padding out their epaulettes as a symbol of grades in the hierarchy. This attempt at intimi-dation can be observed in all known recorded military attire.

In contrast, a woman displays her tiny shoulders with great charm, knowing that her weakness is her strength and will elicit protection and make her protector attracted and attached to her.

There is a general law that animal behaviour experts and sexologists in particular have taught us. This law states that a woman whose strength, be it physical, moral or social, is greater than that of her partner's will end up losing him sooner or later, a victim of sexuality that has lost its *raison d'être*. This law is deeply rooted in man's old primitive brain and cannot be expelled by force, no matter how brutal.

With the hips and pelvis, things are quite different. Here, as if by magic, everything is quite the opposite. Here we have femininity, all curves and magnified. Immediately below the waistline, the hips flare out and widen 'guitar-like' down to the top of the thighs in a curve where the skin thickens. Men are a different shape altogether; their waistlines are less defined and their hips and thighs are straight.

This difference is fundamental and forms my book's central theme. For the time being, we will just take note of this sign. The next chapter will reveal the only real mystery that remains – namely, what caused this difference and how it came about.

Hands

Apart from the lines written by our hands and the actual lines on our hands – and I will leave the graphologists and fortune-tellers to decipher these – our hands convey a whole array of messages.

Their shape and appearance tell us just as much as our facial expressions and we all sense it instinctively. Again, there is very little scientific investigation into this, so we all have to rely on our intuition.

However, gender is the clearest message our hands convey. Like an open book, femininity is written across them. The narrow palms, the tapered fingers, the fleshier skin that covers and hides bumpy bones and protruding tendons, these all make a woman's hand graceful and delicate. Just a glimpse of a tiny finger, raised from a glass while drinking, or of a pearly pink fingernail, and we instantly know that here is a woman.

This simple, natural beauty, to which we are so sensitive, can be enhanced by rings, bracelets and nail varnish but such embellishments are unlikely to mask the broader, heavier hands, and thus true gender, of transvestite men.

Voice

Here is another area where it is difficult to mask our gender for any length of time. As soon as the voice gets involved, any attempt at disguise is doomed to failure. There is something mysterious about a woman's voice that modern electronic synthesizers find hard to reproduce. It does not serve our present purposes to go into any further detail here, but it is useful to know that the voice, produced by the vocal chords, changes during puberty because of our hormones and that depending on which hormone is involved the voice will modulate itself differently, pointing us, once again, in the right gender direction.

Finally, there is one curious anatomical detail: the Adam's apple, which thrills those budding detectives who are eager to work out the hidden gender of the angels. Women have no such protrusion on their larynx and so this is one of those rare occasions when femininity is conspicuous through absence.

Having analyzed and decoded each single distinctive feature in this way, I feel a little guilty at having tracked down every last facet of womanhood. If scientific description wins the day, the poet will be sadly disillusioned. He would definitely be most disappointed to admit that his muse, the subject of his romantic outpourings, would no longer inspire such great feelings if her shoulders were widened by a few centimetres, if a few hairs grew on her face, if the timbre of her voice deepened and her hands grew thicker. It matters little if he is disappointed because, over and beyond his poetry of mysteries, there still remains an enigma that mundane analysis will never even begin to unravel. This is the mystery of how our emotions, our urges, our attractions and our repulsions, and the drive behind our convictions and appetites, are rooted deeply inside us like organs. It is at this level that emotional communication, our most important decisions and our real reasons for living or dying all take place and for no other reason than that given as a covenant by nature.

The beauty and the magic of this mystery are suddenly revealed when we understand how this covenant came about. If we are attracted to a woman because of her eyes, her breasts or her hips this is due to very specific reasons. There is absolutely nothing arbitrary about them. They have been hardwired in us for thousands of generations and they are what the next chapter is all about.

4. Women's curves and sexuality

When I decided to write this book, my intention was to deal with something that had been niggling away at me for ages and had arisen from working with women who I felt were needlessly frustrated while any attempt to reassure them inevitably ended in failure.

I knew then and I know now that I was in possession of the truth. I held on to this conviction because of my medical experience and simply because I was a male representative of my species. However, as soon as I was alone and staring at my blank paper, I quickly realized how difficult it is to demonstrate obvious facts. We have become so familiar with the idea of women's curves, it has become so strongly coloured by our culture and so laden with the received ideas that we accept without any critical examination that I wondered just how I was going to be able to give back to these curves the profound meaning they have always had.

There will never be any discussion about an arm or a leg. Like a body organ, their function has never been hidden or denied, as their purpose is so obvious to everyone that there is no cause for disagreement.

To my mind, women's curves are at least as important. A woman who had no curves whatsoever – and by this I mean pushing my reasoning to the absurd conclusion that her body would be just like a man's – would stand absolutely no chance of finding a partner who would want to make her pregnant. This woman would become artificially sterile, which would spell the end of a long chain of generations fighting for the survival of the species.

In order for women's curves to regain their proper value in your eyes, you needed to understand their purpose and function, which is the reason why I placed them back among the huge repertoire of signals by which the sexes recognize each other.

For readers with no knowledge of the complexities of non-verbal communication, this was a difficult way of tackling the subject and I am still not sure if the message will get across.

I then had the idea of trying a more direct and forceful means of persuasion which might dispel any lingering doubts. We are descended from apes and the fact that we are related to apes who are still around today greatly preoccupies biologists. Within the living world we are no longer isolated on our own island, even though we may be proud of our separateness. Chimpanzees have shown themselves capable of communicating with a sort of human language and as each day passes we grasp a little more of the connection that exists between them and us.

So we were once apes and nowadays we are men. This cannot be disputed. The path that we have followed has made us take giant leaps forward to reach a stage where we now have intelligence and culture. But this is not what interests me. At the same time, our sexuality has undergone radical change and this does concern me enormously because it was while all this upheaval was going on that women's curves made their appearance.

No female ape has the slightest suggestion of breasts, hips or thighs. And it is this perplexing fact that provided me with the decisive argument I was looking for.

If curves appeared in women's bodies then this was because nature had made them part of a more far-reaching plan – she had a new plan for human sexuality. By bestowing this exclusive innovation on woman, nature was giving her the most reliable means possible of getting man to look at her. There can be no other explanation; otherwise it would mean that arbitrariness had crept into evolution's supreme decisions.

This chapter, which opens with these lines, contains the natural history of female sexuality. In it you are going to learn why we are the only living creatures that make love facing each other, along with some even more thought-provoking revelations. This history is of equal interest to men and women. It rarely happens that reading something can be so unsettling that you no longer see things the same way as you did before. And yet this is what happens with this sort of revelation. If we are capable of loving a partner and building ties that are solid enough to withstand time and to create enough warmth and harmony for young offspring to thrive; if a couple has a purpose and if the cement binding them together can endure many bad times, then this is not simply down to our goodwill or the will of the social institutions protecting them. This staying power has far more to do with biological mechanisms, deeply rooted in the primitive areas of our brain, where the laws for our species have been hardwired throughout our prehistory.

The forces that bring us together include women's curves. You may try to close your ears and eyes to this but you cannot stop it from being a fact.

Nature has thought of everything, even your lack of discernment. And some men, at times obsessed because they are ruled by fashions and go along with dictates that rob them of their freedom, still behave as if they were sleepwalking, sometimes sleeping with skinny women but inevitably and quite subconsciously, with their eyes closed and their arms outstretched, they go back to those curves, which they are biologically predestined to embrace.

A brain too large for the female pelvis

All scientists agree that what makes us essentially human is our brain, its possibilities and its particular features. Compared to other species of extinct and living primates, we are the only ones to have a skull containing a brain with a capacity of one thousand four hundred cubic centimetres.

So, and this is a statement of fact, a skull of this size could not negotiate the birth canal through which the foetus passes in the female pelvis.

So either we had to do without this marvellous mutation which offered us so many new possibilities or we had to accept that our young would be born before having reached full neurological maturity. And as you well know we took the latter route.

However, this choice had a consequence that would alter the very essence of human behaviour. A baby that was born immature and incomplete had to then, and still has to today, follow a long path before it can take possession of all its potentialities.

Therefore, when a human being comes into the world he or she is by nature premature.

The female's field of action is restricted by her youngest child

Nature is essentially democratic; what she gives with one hand she takes back with another. We had given birth to a creature endowed with such exceptional potential yet here was this baby, lying on its back, with its eyes closed and its mouth open. A helpless creature, totally and utterly dependent on its mother. At birth, no other animal species has young that are as vulnerable.

Our closest cousins, the chimpanzees, also have their share of immaturity but nature has to some extent found a remedy for this. Baby chimpanzees have been given a few reflexes that if properly used can free the mother from such excessive restrictions.

When it is with its mother, the young baby ape instinctively feels the long hair covering her chest and its tiny hands grab on to this hair. The reflex action is so powerful and her coat so thick that this allows the mother to move around from tree to tree without having to take care of her youngest offspring. If her newborn cannot do very much for itself, it is no great handicap for her and it does not change the way she behaves or how her family group is structured.

It is quite a different matter for human females. Human infants, contrary to all expectations, also have this astonishing primitive reflex, a vestige from our very beginnings that paediatricians call 'grasping'.

To see this reflex all you need do is place an index finger on the open palm of the baby's hands and they will clench tight very strongly. They lock so powerfully on to the fingers that often you can simply lift the baby up out of its cot this way. At feeding times, grasping happens quite spontaneously and, while the baby drinks its milk, its little hands will grasp on to tufts of hair that have long since disappeared.

This reflex action therefore no longer serves any purpose. It is only there to make us dream about times gone by and crazy romping through the African forests when babies grabbed hold of thick coats of hair through which they could nonetheless hear the reassuring sound of their mother's heart.

That it serves no current purpose proves to us that this reflex existed well before we appeared and that if nature sacrificed it this was because she had found a much more suitable way for the human female to raise her young.

While waiting for this innovation to appear, the first human mothers must have had to watch carefully over their young offspring as the savannah was home to many predators.

Obliged to stay around her rudimentary shelter, the female must have resigned herself to being unable to go off with the group of males who went hunting every day. Occasionally, if her children were a little older, she could venture out and pinch a few eggs from nests or pick some wild berries, roots or seeds. However, her movements were strictly limited by the age of her youngest child.

Three hundred grams of meat per person per day

As well as arranging for humankind's children not to be born fully mature, nature also offered it another poisoned chalice which would completely change its future. Already dependent on our mothers, nature also made us dependent on protein.

Biologically, each human being needs eighty grams – about three ounces – of protein per day to live.

Our metabolism can survive without sugars and fats (carbohydrates and lipids); people with diabetes and hypercholesterolaemia who follow their diets correctly have proved this. However, protein is vital for life. We need protein for tissue repair, to heal scars, for our memories to work and for our hair to grow. In particular, growing children need protein as their brains are in the process of developing and the worst time to suffer from protein deficiency is during childhood.

Eighty grams of protein actually equates to three hundred grams of meat, including waste. So a mother with three young children cannot survive for very long without a kilogram, or a couple of pounds, of meat per day. With children so immature and vulnerable and at the same time in desperate need of protein, it meant that logically and inevitably everything came together to create a new choice for the mother. Either she could abandon her children and leave them to die of starvation, or she could ask for help from a man, the great protein-hunter.

It was a no-brainer. And it is from this period onwards, perhaps one or two million years ago, that men took over power. What we are biologically today became slowly hardwired into our genes at a period when, to be a mother, a woman could not survive without the help of a man.

Nowadays, we are unable to fully comprehend this situation; we may find it anachronistic since we can just go into a supermarket and buy powdered protein. However, this programmed structure is within us and could only change if our genes were manipulated.

The chances are that if this sort of change were to happen, women would be freed entirely from male ascendancy, which perhaps no longer has any *raison d'être* left.

But while we wait for this day to arrive, we have to admit that it does exist and that any attempt to disguise it or fight against it requires a lot of effort, and this is likely to upset women's equilibrium and create disharmony within the family.

The sexual connection that brought the family into being

We had reached the point where the female came to ask the male hunter to get protein for her and in particular for her children. What reason might he have had to share with them the spoils of his hunting? None at all, since we have every reason to believe that in such far-off times, the man was still unaware that he was fathering these children. This may appear odd to us but, if we actually think about it, there is no obvious causal link between having sex and becoming pregnant. Even nowadays, there are still some primitive tribes in New Guinea and Australia who have not yet put the two together.

For these first human hunters, children emerged from the females' bodies; they did not belong to them. They were not programmed either to recognize these children or to love them, and certainly not to help them survive by feeding them.

So we had reached a crossroads in our as yet still uncertain existence. The human race faced the threat of extinction for want of humanity. To avoid this disaster, once again nature had to step in and add the last element that would provide the final link in human sexual relations.

What the father would not do for the children he did not acknowledge as his offspring, he had to be made to want to do for the mother.

But for this to happen, it was crucial that the anonymous female became *his* female and that a bond developed between them which was sufficiently intimate. Such a bond had to be close and solid, so that he would go out hunting not just for himself but also to feed these three or four other innocent, vulnerable mouths.

Nature intended this bond to be sexual and between individuals. We know of two species where a similar bond already existed, wild geese and gibbons; both species are capable of living as faithful couples. And it is interesting to note too that both these species share with us the odd monopoly of 'incest taboo'. Once adult, both species never copulate with their mother and rarely with their brothers or sisters. There is still a lot of discussion to be had about this particular characteristic, which according to our most eminent ethnologists forms the cornerstone of our social relationships.

A fundamental difference separates the bond that we required from the one that nature had already developed for geese and gibbons. Neither of these two animal species needs protein to survive and, what is more important, their young very quickly become autonomous. The human infant has to reach its tenth year before it can in part act independently of its mother and it is highly likely that during this time younger brothers and sisters will come along, adding further vulnerable mouths that the hunting father has to provide for.

So the bond had to be sexual, between individuals and, most importantly, permanent. We are now going to see how nature solved this apparently insurmountable difficulty.

The eight sexual conditions that made human love possible

The long, inventive journey that culminated in the human infant very nearly got no further than its cradle. Its brain, full of so many future possibilities, came up against an obstacle – its inevitable dependency on protein and its dependency on a selfish male.

Nature would not give up on her most wonderful invention. Seeing that for the first time ever the mother was not enough, nature went about providing a father. To do this, she devised eight modifications that radically changed human sexual relations.

1.The only female that is always available for sex

For all mammals, the love-making season is a long-awaited event that livens up their humdrum lives. They hunt, they feed and they sleep. They are born and they die under the tropical sun and, above all, they impatiently and eagerly await the first signs of their females coming into heat.

Some species are very lucky and this lively period comes round fairly frequently. This is true for certain rodents such as mice; their gestation periods are rapid and frequent and female rabbits are receptive eight to ten times a year.

The elephant is much worse off and has to wait almost five years. Contraception is certainly not an elephant's main worry.

Monkeys had already achieved a great innovation by inventing oestrus and, thanks to this, female monkeys became receptive five days every month around ovulation.

Human females had reached the same point too, but this was not enough to keep a male for good. Nature made one last effort and transformed woman into a super-female who would be completely receptive on a permanent basis. What an amazing godsend for all those males who had not yet invented television! It was good to go off hunting but it was also great to get back to the horde and to those females who no longer bit you if you sneakily tried to mount them from behind. The only challenge was to be one of the first males home so as to be sure of finding a female who was still available. The strongest and most dominant males were, of course, the ones who were best looked after.

Already this first measure had made the males less selfish but it did not always make it any easier for those mothers with lots of young children, as the males were still very reluctant to feed so many unknown mouths. So once again, nature had to further innovate and find a way of making the relationship more personal.

2. The only female to make love from the front

Up until now, all female creatures on earth had attracted their males from behind. So it was not in any way surprising that all the sexual signals female monkeys sent out were to be found on their lower back. A well-rounded behind, nice and pink and shiny, visible from afar in all weathers. Two hemispheres where not a single hair grew that might lessen their impact. And, just underneath, a well-defined vulva, with small and large crimson red lips – like a beacon sending out a powerful signal. And finally, to really get the message across, some powerful apocrine glands that gave off a musky smell for any slightly short-sighted males.

Together, these messages ended up channelling the male's powerful virility into a vortex that culminated in the female's behind. This meant, therefore, that love-making was anonymous and one behind was just as good as any other.

Once it was over, the female got on with her business, and if the male had been given satisfaction, he would not even know which female he owed this to.

Nature's second innovation spelled an end to this bizarre, anonymous relationship. Primates have always had ways of recognizing each other. All experts agree upon this fact since they know that primates recognize each other from facial features. Eyes and gesticulations are so varied that there can be no possibility of confusion. So nature waved her magic wand for a second time and woman, now standing upright, looked her male in the face. It is from this day on that man has known *who* is giving him his pleasure. Lying on top of his woman the whole time he had sexual contact with her, man was able, with his eyes open, to mentally link the crescendo of his sexual emotions and his exaltation as his orgasm pulsated through him with the specific features of his female. This meant that at last copulation became associated with an individual, making a basis for attachment possible. If the word really does have any meaning, then it was on this day that we actually started to make 'love'.

But that was not the end of it. For this miracle to become a part of daily life, it had to undergo some adjustments. To be able to make love facing each other, the couple had to be attracted to one another from the front and primarily from the front. It would no longer be quite decent to be attracted by round, pink buttocks and big red vaginal lips and then suddenly at the very last moment swap things around and have face-to-face sex.

In order to give the whole score greater harmony, sexual signals also had to be triggered from the front of the body. And this is indeed what happened, because nature is consistent and leaves nothing to chance.

3. The only female to have permanent breasts

For millions of years, primates had been attracted by round, pink buttocks, two tempting hemispheres laden with sensual delight. A message as old as this could not be forgotten overnight. The message had to be preserved. So nature invented something along the same lines; adding two rounded, curved breasts right across the female chest which a male could not fail to notice. You wanted curves and you wanted two lots, then you can have them and as soon as puberty starts. Note how this undulation appears quietly, starts to protrude and then quickly fills out. Other apes also have teats but they come and go and are only there while the animal is lactating, a period during which the female is not receptive and when her milk glands are more likely to turn any males away from her.

Apart from its role as a sexual embellishment, the human breast as it is now actively contributes to the sexual act itself. As the female grows excited, the breast swells and becomes protuberant. It can swell to up to 25 per cent of its volume. As soon as it is caressed, the nipple becomes erect and can double in length. It also grows wider and its pigmented colour deepens. Moreover, and this confirms its role as a sexual organ, the breast becomes very erogenous and many women say that they are able to reach orgasm simply by having their nipples touched.

The fact that this organ hinders all movements of the shoulder provides further confirmation. Because of its weight and its position at the base of the arm, the breast gets in the way of wide-ranging movements. Sports doctors are quite adamant that female tennis players have difficulty with their serve essentially because of their mammary glands. If evolution was happy for women to put up with this sort of handicap, it was because the bosom was now a permanent part of its magical formula for female sexuality and this more than compensated for any lack of movement. These permanent, conspicuous breasts are therefore quite some innovation, and it is unthinkable that a modification on this scale, totally dependent on female hormones, would not have a role to play as sexual trigger. Whatever culture or civilization we bring to mind, whenever a man sees a beautiful pair of breasts he invariably feels a thrill and a flicker of excitement. We do not need to prove it as this is what the whole of humanity has been doing for such a long time.

4. A pair of lips that are a reminder of other lips

Female primates give off a second sexual signal with their large vaginal lips which stand out between the female monkey's two brown, hairy thighs. These lips can only be seen from behind, but are permanently visible on these females who live and move around 'on all fours'.

This signal, which had so long thrilled the savannahs, was lost forever to woman once she was able to stand up. However, the configuration had such power of attraction and was so firmly rooted in man's sexual mechanisms that it could not simply vanish without leaving any trace. Now that the vaginal opening was hidden from view, there appeared in the middle of the face and surrounding the mouth other exaggerated lips, which retained their sexual nuance because they bore a certain resemblance.

Primates have a mouth that is nothing more than a dry opening used only for feeding. They never have the pink and full, fleshy and raised edges to their mouth that turn human lips into a pure sexual embellishment.

Indeed, if we leave aside nails for the upholsterer and needles for the seamstress, both of whom use their lips to free up their hands, for our species this organ no longer fulfils any purpose whatsoever. Why we should have lips at all would be incomprehensible if they had not found some other focus – sexual orality and a new occupation, kissing.

However, we also need to recognize that although lips have very clear sexual connotations for our species, women do not have the monopoly on this magnetic marker as men's lips have the power to move women too.

As far as I know, lips are the only erogenous signal that is completely bisexual. Yet could kissing, such an intrinsically human activity, ever have helped us communicate if a woman's fleshy lips had not been able to fasten on to their masculine equivalent?

5. The magic circle of hips and thighs

With the breasts and lips message now in place, the front of the human female had become attractive. The reversal meant that these signals could just get on with playing their part. With a single look, a man could register and recognize individual facial features and sexual charms without there being any ambiguity over identity. But not everything was in place and the play was far from over. To get to the finale, the crowning act that would mean the species could be renewed over and over again, the man also had to know where to put his seed. He recognized the frontage to the entrance, now he needed to know where the door was so that he could open it and enter in. In other words, since looking at a woman from the front meant that the vulva was no longer visible, another signal had to be created to replace it. All pre-existing materials had already been used; we now had to be totally innovative. So at this precise moment in our sexual revolution, the decisive, exclusively human invention came about that is perhaps the core of my book's thesis.

Take a woman who is standing up and looking at you face on, and think of the entrance to her vulva as being the centre of operations. With a compass, trace a circle with a twenty-centimetre – eight-inch – radius. This circle will encompass the belly button, the upper curve of the hips, then continue along the curve of the thighs – the curve that nowadays is sometimes referred to as 'jodhpur thighs'. This imaginary circle is there in male and female primates too but there is nothing special about it to attract attention.

However, it is here, in this neutral territory, that there suddenly appears a magical glimpse of the final change the female body will undergo.

This circle will suddenly grow rounder, become permeated with adipose tissue, fill out and firm up. It is only woman who acquired this innovation which without any shadow of a doubt sets her apart from man. Yet this innovation would serve no purpose if the male's structures had not at the same time been programmed to be sexually aware of it. His eyes are therefore drawn to this new signal, and informed by his sense of touch his hands now feel the taut, firm texture of these fleshy parts. Nature plays a magnificent game of chess with the human male's bewildered senses, as it is right here, among these curves he can see and touch, that the queen is hidden away.

If men have ever preferred their women with curves then it was definitely this day that they chose to resolve the matter. And if, millions of years later, caught up in our mumble-jumble of cultures and fashions, we are puzzling over the hidden meaning of these curves then it is because our eyes have grown weak from reading our sorcerer's apprentice books and we have forgotten the amazing message in these magical curves.

This book has a purpose and a goal: to restore women's curves, which are in man's heart, to their rightful place. To repudiate this message is a little like saying no to the most wonderful innovation nature ever devised to seal our human bond.

6. The first female primate without hair

An identifiable face, a mouth with its two red, full lips, two breasts, hemispherical and full, which bring to mind the vulva and the buttocks respectively, rounded curvaceous hips and thighs that form a magnetic circle and centre on the entrance to the vagina – with the major work complete, all that remained was to add the finishing, decorative touches. The signals were good but not yet perfect.

It is more or less around this period that the human female lost her hair. For a long time, scientists who study evolution have wondered what could have been the point of this mutation. If woman is the only female mammal not to have hair then there has to be some very good reason for this. The human baby still has its grasping reflex action, but its mother no longer has any hair it can cling on to. If we are deprived of the terms of this equation then this is because the innovation offered us a greater advantage. Desmond Morris, author of *The Naked Ape,* an eminent ethologist who knows what he is talking about and whose work for a long time focused on our species' nakedness, was the first person to suggest the role that this mutation may have played in marking out sexual signals.

What indeed would be the point of having this new, permanent bosom if it was to remain hidden away behind a screen of long, brown hair? And the point of these beautifully shaped lips if concealed by a beard? Even the hips and thighs would only make up a bogus magic circle and the wonderful elastic firmness of the flesh would be lost if it was scrunched up underneath lots of hair.

The first striptease in the history of humanity started with this sudden biological depilation and perhaps this is how woman appeared in her final state of nakedness.

Some comparative anatomy experts have sought to claim that hair vanished as a way of adapting to climate change and that the human hunter must have got very hot chasing after prey under the tropical sun. This argument does not cut much ice once you realize that leopards and cheetahs have kept their coats intact, predators that are far more fleet of foot than man.

This hypothesis would certainly offer no explanation as to why man, who goes out hunting for his woman, should have more hair than her. The only possible, logical reason is that it has to do with human sexuality. Being naked exposes women's attractions and shows them off to their best advantage. If nowadays a woman dresses with such care then it is to better undress in front of the man she wants to seduce.

The only hair that she did retain covered areas either with no distinctive sexual feature, such as arms or legs, or those which by contrast were there to attract attention. This is true of the pubic triangle which is located, as if by chance, right on target as the bull's-eye of the magic circle of her hips and thighs. No one is in any doubt about the suggestive power of this tiny triangle of hair; on fashionable beaches every last covering has been discarded except the final bikini triangle that conceals this powerful trigger signal.

There still remains a last tuft under the arms that resisted as hair did a vanishing trick. As we have already seen, by trapping smells, hair plays a vital role for women. All primates who focus sexually on behinds have aphrodisiac smells that also emerge from the rear. They emanate from little glands distributed around the vulva and anus and all apes have a bit of a sniff there before inserting their penis.

This scented message is still there in man in a vestigial form, but it has much diminished in intensity and, should it still happen to serve a purpose, it is always a surprise to discover it. In an embrace where the man is looking at his woman in the face, whatever smells are being sent out from behind often get to him too late. On the other hand, any smells trapped in underarm hair can easily reach the man's nose and play their part in maintaining his level of arousal.

For our modern cultures, hell-bent on eradicating all germs, sexual scents have a bad reputation. This is a mystery that I am unable to solve.

It is claimed that Henry IV of France forbade his mistresses to wash. This footnote from our kings' history is of sufficient importance to have been handed down to us and, if this is what the monarch did, then there is no reason to believe that his subjects did not also follow suit. The seventeenth century had not yet outlawed body odours. Nowadays it is unseemly to sniff and it is depressing to see all the effort and hard work that goes into producing chemical deodorants so that we can cover up our natural scents which all have highly specialized functions.

Ear, nose and throat specialists are well aware that our sense of smell is totally bound up with our sexuality. They often treat male impotency and low libido by electrically stimulating the mucous membranes associated with smell.

Musk is a scented ester that all mammals secrete during the love-making season. *Muscadins* was the name given to young French dandies who without a second thought made a great show of using musk to its full advantage.

Times have indeed changed and if it is clear that we are now living in a period where our culture is hyper-sexualized, this is through excessive hype and promotion of an eroticism that is only visual.

The image rules supreme and our children no longer scurry away from the television once the watershed hour is passed. My role here is not to discuss the choices made by our Western culture, but simply to point out the total lack of balance that has arisen between our visual world and our scent world. It would no doubt take another book to determine the reasons for this large-scale sterilization of smells which has been inflicted on our women and this pseudo-healthy hygiene regime that involves spending time in the shower and then applying some chemical exfoliator to every part of the body where any scent or smell may linger. And once you are quite sure that absolutely nothing natural or personal remains then you can apply some fashionable fragrance that everyone else is wearing on their skin.

If we intend to force this model of cleanliness into our collective subconscious, then it is a trap that every doctor can and should expose. However, we must bring our discussion of sexual scents to an end, otherwise it will take us off at too great a tangent. All we need to know is that, as with curves, men simply grin and bear it. They are happy to play along with society's game, abiding by the rules laid down by the taboos of the day and renouncing women's curves and smells. However, subconsciously men are still thrilled by them. And those women skinny enough to epitomize the emaciated ideals of thinness and those women who are so deodorized and sterilized that they lose a good part of their sexuality are at times astonished – but always a little too late – to see their husbands or lovers fall for a more natural and fulfilled woman who smells healthy and alive.

7. The amazing world of women's pupils

Reading the history of our human sexual revolution as I have described it to you, you may well think that it is allegorical and possibly romanticized and that I have added in enough ingredients to make it palatable. This is not the case at all. What you have read about how femininity appeared is the most likely scenario and the one that best fits with currently available ethological and anthropological data.

The various transformations and the forms they took were perhaps not as simplified as this, but we would have needed a complete volume to track an evolutionary process that covered at least one million years. However, we can be certain about one thing: our ancestors were primates who looked like present-day anthropoid apes. There is not a scientist on earth who would contradict me on this. And what is even more certain is that we are today what we are. We know where we started out from and where we have got to. The methods that nature used to cover this distance can only be similar to the methods that she normally uses to create. And the logic behind her evolutionary progress, with which we are well acquainted from having studied it and used it to form laws for the rest of the animal world, cannot all of a sudden change on the pretext that it is humankind that we are talking about here.

This preamble to reassure you that we really are describing reality will now reveal its ultimate purpose, because we are going to look at a phenomenon so astonishing and so unusual that it could almost have come straight out of a fictional romance.

In 1967, Eckhard Hess, a professor of psychology at the University of Chicago, made a remarkable discovery which caused a great stir among traditional psychology conformists and continues to do so today.

Apart from its surprising beauty, this discovery is of particular interest to us since it adds a little more weight to the theory of individuals bonding through having sexual relations while looking each other in the eye.

Eckhard Hess knew that the pupil in the human eye is there to control light, and that we all have a reflex action that makes our pupils contract in the sun and dilate in the shade. But what nobody realized, and what he by accident discovered, was that pupils had to have some additional purpose because when exposed to the same amount of light they showed significant variations in diameter.

Hess put forward the hypothesis that our pupils open and shut depending on the attraction or repulsion we feel for the object or person we are looking at.

In the American context, at a time when all psychology was steeped in culturalist dogmas, his hypothesis was scandalous. How could anyone have an attraction or repulsion reflex without having analyzed logically and rationally the reasons that would make us react this way? To put such a hypothesis forward was likely to get you ostracized from the scientific community.

So Hess was careful and forced himself to stick to very rigorous experiments. He worked with students of both sexes and he projected in front of them a huge number of photographs showing all kinds of artefacts, people and situations. At the same time he measured, in an extremely precise way, the slightest change to their pupils. The results spoke for themselves, confirming without any shadow of a doubt the crazy hypothesis he had started out from.

When shown photos of the countryside, monuments or objects with no particular emotional meaning, the pupils of the male students did not change. However, a photo of a naked woman slipped in among the others triggered rapid dilation whereas a photo of a naked man had no effect on the eye.

In getting the female students' pupils to dilate, photos of naked men and smiling babies tied for first prize. This was true even for female students who had never had any children. It was interesting to note that the male students did not react to pictures of babies.

This totally subconscious emotional reflex action of the pupils confirmed that we have deep-rooted innate capabilities such as our sexual instinct or a nascent maternal instinct. Such ideas were very badly received and attempts were made to consign the professor's scandalous experiments to obscurity.

Eckhard Hess did, nonetheless, confirm his experiments; he gave them careful thought and wrote a book entirely devoted to his research, which he published for the general public with the title *The Tell-Tale Eye: How Your Eyes Reveal Hidden Thoughts and Emotions*. This book provides us with a second and even more astounding revelation than the first one, explaining as it does the function and role of this reflex action in human communication and our sexual relations, which is why it is of such great importance to us.

When a woman sees a man she likes and desires, her pupils dilate. This has already been proven. However, what is new is that while looking at her, the man will perceive that her pupils are dilating, quite subconsciously of course (and this is precisely the definition of Konrad Lorenz's 'instinctive trigger'). This perception sends a message to his primitive brain that his conscious computer brain cannot understand. And while searching in vain for the reason for his emotion, the man will tell himself what we have all so often said or heard others say, 'There's something about the way she looks.' This proves, if indeed we needed any proof, that we do not know what it is. Hess proved this second part of the communication process by using two identical photos showing the face of the same woman. However, one photo had been retouched to slightly enlarge the aperture of her pupils. Although it was indiscernible, this slight adjustment was all it took for a significant proportion of the men to prefer the retouched photo.

Lastly, Eckhard Hess presented his final revelation by proving that the man who feels emotion because of this modification, which he perceives without being aware of it, reacts in turn by dilating his own pupils too.

The communication chain was complete; without any ambiguity, it explained why during sexual encounters it is fundamentally important for us to look at one another. We can now understand so many things that once seemed magical or inexplicable to us. What is beautiful in a woman's eyes is in part connected with the subconscious welcome she is offering us.

This is now my own personal conjecture, but it may explain why light eyes (blue, green or hazel) are generally more popular than dark eyes (black or brown). The pupil, which is naturally always an intense black, contrasts strongly against a very light iris. The slightest change in the pupil can be detected from afar. Eyes with a dark iris are not as easy to read and their beauty will certainly be less praised as they 'do not lay their cards on the table'. However, as has been said since time immemorial, what such eyes may lose in attraction they gain in mystery and depth. The fact that dark eyes provide little contrast and do not give away their first impressions so readily confirms this proverbial statement.

All of which no doubt explains as well why for a very long time courtesans would alter the way their eyes looked by adding drops of belladonna to them; belladonna has a long-lasting dilating effect on the pupils. They did this to increase their powers of seduction – which amply compensated for making their vision blurry, which at times must have been quite a godsend.

It may also offer an explanation as to why we find so disturbingly ambiguous the way that serious heroin addicts look. Their pupils are permanently extremely dilated, becoming exaggerated to the point of caricature and making their addiction plain to see.

It is an acknowledged fact that Chinese jade sellers watch their clients' pupils to work out what price they will ask. Turkish traders always wear dark glasses when buying their carpets to make sure they do not divulge any information regarding their intentions.

To sum up, our pupils' little reflex action tells us a great deal about the extent to which we have been programmed. Communication through the pupils allows us to know just how receptive our long-standing partner or new conquest is feeling. No ape has this marvellous reflex and it provides the final proof that, if we stood up on our legs and if we make love facing one another, then the reason for this is to know for sure who we are making love with and to stay with the woman who gives us the most satisfaction.

8. The only female to experience orgasms

We have almost reached the end of our long investigation into the means that nature chose to create our long-lasting sexual bond. We have watched this bond grow richer with each new acquisition and we have almost reached the point where we can actually call it human love. There was just one final but essential modification that woman still needed – to be able to achieve orgasm.

We have a strange propensity for projecting our consciousness on to the way animals behave, anthropomorphism, which means we labour under the false illusion that most female animals also get their pleasure during copulation. This could not be further from the truth. If we just consider primates, which we are too, no female great ape has ever experienced an orgasm.

Her dramatic behaviour when she is in heat is only blind, instinctive tension which drives her subconsciously to behave sexually. In just a few seconds and a dozen or so thrusts, a male baboon or chimpanzee will have got his pleasure but his partner will have had absolutely no satisfaction at all and, without even turning round, off she will go to find other males that are in just as much of a hurry.

If such behaviour had continued among the human species, it would have threatened to bring tumbling down the enormous construct put in place to seal our permanent sexual bond.

Nature found a remedy for this by giving the human female what no other female creature on earth could ever obtain – an orgasm.

It is highly likely that this is the most recent innovation of a sexual nature that humans have undergone.

To back this up, evolutionists base their arguments on how fragile and hugely variable the female orgasm is. In terms of evolution, the male orgasm is a very old invention and may date back hundreds of millions of years. It is a reliable reflex, one that is firmly implanted in the spinal chord and cannot be much modified by any cultural changes. The female orgasm is labile and delicate; to achieve it requires some concentration and even some fantasizing.

Current opinion confirms this when it asserts that women are more 'cerebral' than men, which tells us a lot about how fragile the female orgasm is. Sexology statistics will only state with certainty that 50 per cent of women between twenty-five and thirty achieve orgasm.

Coming back to what interests us: nature had worked hard on woman, making her sexually attractive face on, and getting her to develop erogenous signals more or less all over so that males would be stimulated and motivated.

To finish off its work, evolution had four good reasons to give women orgasms:

- Woman had asked man for help for her immature children who were desperate for protein. The man had gone along with this because his attachment to his woman had now become personal. However, nature could not tolerate woman being a mere prostitute even if she were degrading herself simply to ensure her children's survival. The man would indeed provide protein, but he would provide pleasure too and this perhaps explains why, of all the primates, man has the biggest and the longest penis.

- The second reason was to complete the sexual communication circle. From now on, face to face, each partner would get their pleasure and show that they got it in all sorts of ways. This would help cement the personalized relationship, the bond and their love full stop.

- The third reason is far more banal. Since an orgasm brings about an intense nervous release, for quite some time afterwards it leaves the woman spent and she may even fall asleep. For a species that stands upright, this time spent resting horizontally is absolutely necessary for fertilization. Once copulation is over, a female ape may, if she so desires, busy herself with other things. The semen she has just received will remain inside her because she moves around on all fours. Since a woman stands upright, force of gravity alone is bound to hamper her chances of fertilization.

- Finally, as the female orgasm takes longer to achieve than the male orgasm, the man may well be tempted to have a second go at bringing his woman to climax – evolution's way of rewarding mothers of large families with an extra gift.

Conclusion

We have now completed our investigation into biological femininity. The animals have spoken to us with the only language they know, that of instinct and non-verbal communication. Their entire sexuality depends on trigger signals. The animal side that is still there within us continues to express itself using this same language. One of these messages is a woman's curves, as is the silk moth's smell, the stickleback's bloated stomach and the pigeon's cooing.

I next traced how female sexuality came about. This revolution made woman cross a dividing line that no other animal has even come close to.

Since she stands upright, woman is the only female creature who makes love looking her partner in the face and the only one who is permanently available. For her to be given this privilege and to keep it, her sexual trigger signals had to move from the back to the front of her body. It was at this precise time that her curves became apparent, with their enormous advantages – round breasts, curved hips, shapely thighs, shaped lips, round pupils and round nipples. What is more, her curves also had a firmness; shapely curves that are taut, elastic, firm and full and which fit the hand of a man, for whom their message is intended and who will make no mistake. With this plenitude, his hand finds a way of exploring all its sensory possibilities; it can play for the sheer delight of his senses as it works out what is hidden away behind the soft covering.

But woe betide any bone that juts out without protection. Shame upon any protruding tendons or muscles that can be seen and cannot conceal their toughness. Bones, tendons and muscles, which underpin energy and strength, may be used in situations of conflict. A man who approaches a woman sexually must on no account see or feel them as they are symbols of confrontation, whereas love is a symbol of peace. *No sexual act is possible unless the woman conceals whatever strength she has within her.* Before she lies down in bed, she must forget all about her weapons or conceal them so that the man cannot touch or see them. He will inspect this body that delights him and search everywhere for any possible weapons; he will examine and explore it all over to be sure that he can give himself over completely by losing some of his consciousness and his strength.

The legend of Delilah, who cut off Samson's hair while he was asleep, is in every man's heart. Symbolically, a hand that rests on hips and thighs which are not shapely enough and which do not conceal the solidity of their bone and the strength of their muscle will mean this hand is on alert. The man will not be at rest; he will not be in thrall to woman's shapeliness and her curves. Inside him, the aggressive beast that cohabits with the sexual beast will not allow him to give himself totally to his partner. The orgasm that he achieves will not be as deep, as complete or as spontaneous as it should be. The role of women's curves is to separate these two forces dividing human motivations. Symbolically their job is to put the aggressive beast to sleep, to hypnotize it, to disarm it, to subjugate it and to make it die just for a moment so that our splendid sexual animality, freed from all qualms, can lose itself in woman.

All our sexual mythology is based upon this symbolic opposition.

Man is strong, hard, sinewy, muscular, bony, hairy and bearded. His behaviour is more aggressive, more straightforward, inflexible and protective.

Woman is smooth, delicate, soft, beardless and hairless – naked in other words; weak, she needs security and protection; she is peaceful and curvaceous.

Women's curves are therefore not just some mere anatomical feature but a basic part of her femininity, both physically and mentally. Any attempt to discredit them is not just an aberration but an offence to sexuality and to nature, who intended women to be shaped this way.

This is the final message that I wanted to get across in part one, dealing with women and nature. I might have been able to say it in a couple of lines and some of you may think this would have done the trick. You could not be more wrong. There are some obvious truths that we strangle daily with our own hands because we want to be sure of not succumbing to their appeal. I am still convinced that it was absolutely necessary to spend some time looking at what animals can tell us and to go back to the sources of our sexual evolution.

In part two, devoted to women and culture, I am going to tell you how the scandal was perpetrated and by whom; how something as fundamentally feminine as women's curves could be misrepresented, discredited and eventually inverted; and what most women in the West have had to put themselves through, subconsciously, to reach a state where they hanker after awkward, thin, curve-free bodies.

The purpose of my book is not to philosophize on women's biological nature. I am attempting something more concrete. I am writing as a nutritionist, who on a daily basis sees the damaging effects caused by the desperate struggle to be thin. For the women who succeed I can see what is heroic in this struggle; and I see what is frustrating for the women who fail.

By offering technical and psychological support, I become involved in their struggle so I know how long and painful it can be. This is why I want to take to task those women who 'crusade without a cross', those who quite happily starve themselves only to end up all skin and bone and famished, in bed with a husband or lover who never in a million years wanted any of this. I firmly believe that women's curves are being persecuted because of a pact made with *flatness*; and constantly on the prowl around flatness are frigidity and impotence.

Part Two

WOMEN'S CURVES
AND CULTURE

At the end of part one, I was firmly convinced that I had used all the natural and biological arguments at my disposal to restore some seriousness to the idea of women's curves.

So I hope that you no longer have any remaining doubts about the *value* of these curves; biologists must not be the only people to be convinced of their usefulness. Women's curves are not cultural data that can fit in or not with what a society chooses. They are a universal for all women and appear during puberty along with periods and pubic hair, changes in the voice, the first signs of breasts and the first feminine body odours.

Alongside all these other outward signs, women's curves send out an initial message that lets you know in no uncertain terms that the young girl of twelve or thirteen whom you considered to be a child is now turning into a woman. Even if fathers appear oblivious to what is happening, mothers are quite well aware as they start talking about forbidden fruit and the pill.

The second message is more eloquent and is certainly not meant for the young woman's parents. It is aimed at the eyes of boys, perhaps not yet at their hands, but that will not be a long time coming. In all its naïvety, this message is saying:

'These curves that you can see taking shape, these breasts, these hips, these thighs, take a good look and don't think about anything. In these few centimetres that set us apart lies a trap which you cannot even begin to imagine and which is working away on my behalf to maximum effect.' This is what her sexuality, which 'triggers signals' without giving any reason, is actually saying.

So the situation is clear. The woman displays her distinctive assets. The man notices them and the emotions he feels would have us believe that communication between them is going to take place just as it takes place among all known species and all civilizations until we reach our own. You do not need to be a shrewd observer to see that by rejecting their curves, women in the West are now deliberately sabotaging these early stages of sexual communication.

We know of other situations where women have ended up altering some part of their animal legacy – for example, by using bottle feeding or contraception. But at least there were sound logical reasons here; her independence and comfort increased immeasurably; her children did not come out of it at all badly as she had a happy family that was easier to bring up. However, with our case in point, women's refusal to accept their curves makes no sense at all and throws up a strange problem that this section will deal with.

Before I even start, I have to say that if I look at things from a purely biological perspective, I believe that the irrational aversion to women's curves is seriously detrimental to both sexes.

So let us analyze what is going on and find out who stands to gain from this crime of lese-nature. I can reassure you straightaway that women are not to blame. The people responsible are elsewhere and, without wishing to whet your appetite, I can tell you they are well hidden and operate behind the scenes. This section will also be about unmasking them. Pursuing them will not just be some trivial game, because to make them own up we will need to track them down and it is quite likely that while we are on their trail we will uncover some things that are not always reassuringly fragrant.

So we will start off by examining the party that has been attacked – in other words, the female body – and we will establish what the current canons are for this mutilated femininity. It will be easy to compare these with the canons of other cultures and civilizations where they functioned quite innocently.

Then we will examine the consequences of this nature–culture conflict and just how detrimental they are to men and women today.

The chapter that will be most surprising is the one in which we will examine the causes that have driven women subconsciously to sink their own ship by rejecting one of the most wonderful and most reliable means nature has given them of attracting the opposite sex. This self-mutilation revolves around a combination of toxic cultural facts which tell us a great deal about how our civilization is running out of steam.

The people responsible will then be exposed and you will be surprised to learn that you always looked upon them as your most dependable allies.

5. A panorama of ideas about women's curves

Very often, part of my work involves consultations with women who want to lose weight or volume. What strikes me most is that I can detect great differences in what motivates them to take these steps. To the uninitiated, weight and volume may seem like similar ideas but they make most women react in very different ways.

Weight is a neutral, purely quantitative concept. Being overweight is annoying because it makes everything involved with living your daily life awkward to do. If weight is evenly spread out it can be tolerated for quite some time, so a woman who refuses to be overweight and makes up her mind to do something about it has definitely reached a limit beyond which she feels uncomfortable.

Volume is a qualitative concept and the curves I am talking about have far more to do with how they are distributed over the body than actual body mass. A woman with curves is not a fat woman; she is a woman whose body has all the right parts, who has breasts, hips and thighs that flag up her femininity perfectly. And yet, it is these specifically feminine markers that are subject to the most extreme aversion.

Whenever I ask a woman why she wants to reduce the volume of her thighs, I notice that for a moment she looks surprised and hesitant. Then she gives me a rather odd look, as if she did not get the question. Surely it ought to be glaringly obvious? And most of the time the woman just glances down at her thighs and feels them as a way of pointing out to me that my question was a stupid one.

However, since by nature I am curious, I refuse to give up so I ask her: 'Perhaps it's something your husband doesn't like?'

It is a question that tends to elicit a knowing smile, which says a lot about this poor chap who is quite definitely in the dark about what his wife is up to.

And if it is a young girl who has come for a consultation I cannot stop myself from asking her if her hips are preventing her from having relationships with boys of her age. Paradoxically the answer is always no.

So I press on with a little questioning because I would like to get a rational answer but am still waiting for one: 'So is it for your colleagues at work, your friends or your family?'

And, like a leitmotif, I keep getting the inevitable reply, as if all these women had agreed upon it among themselves: 'But doctor, it's for me, for me when I look at myself in a mirror. These thighs, these hips, they're horrible, ugly. Surely you can see that?'

So there we have it – collective hypnosis continues to hold sway. And there is nothing left for me to say.

There was a time when I tried to offer arguments, understand and even challenge what I was hearing by suggesting that these curves might be attractive and that they were absolutely natural. However, I have given up on this for two very specific reasons.

First of all, I kept coming up against a wall and I realized there was a conscious narrative talking to me about appearances while a subconscious narrative was reciting a firmly embedded cultural dictate, so deeply rooted that I could not reach it.

The second reason is far simpler. If I went on about it too much I felt that my arguments might be misinterpreted and my patients might think they were becoming a little too personal.

So it was because of my work, from listening to what these women were telling me day in and day out, that I realized just how brainwashed they all were. However, my position as an observer is a particularly privileged one. I am convinced that very few men have any idea about the extent to which these women suffer. Some men, with whom I have discussed it, just smile back at me. How could any woman feel so much resentment about having a good pair of thighs or well-padded hips?

And breasts, these wonders that are in such short supply! Surely you are dramatizing things! Yet, I see all too well when I am dining with friends and this sort of conversation crops up over pudding that most women do not take issue with these assertions.

Over time, and by adopting a softly-softly approach, I learnt that this aversion to their curves, which all sorts of women feel to a greater or lesser degree and regardless of which class they belong to, was often kept as a secret and not divulged to men.

There is a sort of modesty here, and I perceive some inconsistency, some faint glimpses of lucidity; some clear-sightedness does exist which stops me from giving up hope altogether.

If women feel some shame in confessing that they want nothing to do with their curves, then a little common sense and censure still prevail, preventing these women from falling completely under the spell of cultural dictates.

It is in this direction and into this barely visible breach that we must move and unmask the deception in an attempt to reverse a trend that continues to attract followers.

To do this, we need to start by turning the spotlight on different views of women. How we see women at this moment in time in the West is not how they have always been seen in other climes and in other times. And even nowadays I believe I can say without risk of contradiction that France is the country most scarred by this diktat and that the French are in part responsible for devising and exporting this plague.

Current canons regarding the female shape

The great curse of any culture is to believe that it is the repository of truth. And what holds true for great culture, for ideologies and religions, also holds true for lesser culture. Today most women in the West imagine that they have reached the end of the trajectory leading to the definitive female archetype.

Any disinterested observer only has to cast a quick glance elsewhere and at what came before to be wryly amused. I am not going to simply cast a glance; I am going to rummage and delve wherever we can still uncover evidence to prove that how we view things today is but one page in the book of humanity's history and its fashions.

However, before doing this, let us work out exactly how we currently see the female body. What is the current feminine archetype in the Western world?

I have two sources of information for this: my own experience working as a nutritionist, which over time equates to a mini-survey, which has been greatly supplemented by my own interest in the matter extending far beyond my work.

Most importantly, I have information provided by the enormous sounding board of the media, by the vast range of different magazines, by cinema, television and advertising and by figurative, pictorial art.

Fashions in clothing also reflect what is being worn and by extension the sort of body that has to wear such clothes. And I see that what is being introduced into current dictates for femininity presents us first of all with:

The image of a *tall* and slender woman. It is fashionable today to be at least one metre seventy centimetres – five foot six inches – tall. Scarcely fifty years ago, such a height was considered gigantic, as even the average Frenchman would hardly have measured up to it.

And yet there is no model worthy of the name who would dare admit to being under this limit. I have myself gone through the catalogues of three well-known agencies that deal with this type of fashion professional and I had great difficulty finding six models, out of a total of seventy, who were under one metre sixty-eight centimetres – five foot five inches – tall.

The *waist* is slim. But far less so than during the period when women wore off-the-shoulder dresses and were advised to strap themselves into corsets to get that famous hourglass figure, which, incidentally, had no other purpose than to enhance the contours of the hips. So now we have a waist that is free from constraint.

Breasts are the first part of the body to be affected by this taboo on curves. They should not be too much in evidence. However, given the difficulty in finding enough women to fit with this new imperative, which biologically is scarcely imaginable, women are advised to hide their breasts away, to compress them; or those poor 'unfortunate' women with big breasts are simply told to wear baggy, loose-fitting clothing.

However, this blatant attempt at brainwashing comes up against a powerful, biological antidote. Insofar as they are ornamental, women quite happily give in and reject their breasts but at times they also see that these same breasts play a role in breast-feeding. And to some extent, this mutes the possible discredit some misogynistic designers try to graft on to these parts of the body to which many of us still owe our lives.

There is therefore a certain flexibility to the canon's rigidity and male homage is so intense, so direct and so immediate that some women still manage to keep a cool enough head to defiantly sport their bosoms. However, we are far removed from the days when post-war Italian actresses displayed their charms with such pride.

I find that my opinions are borne out by the way bras have changed so radically over recent years. We have moved from rigid under-wired structures that made the bosom stick out to flexible elastic support then to support that is simply decorative. And nowadays it is common to just wear nothing at all. Women's lingerie is dying through lack of nourishment, so it seeks out new markets with fancy bits of underwear that sexualize women.

Generous-sized breasts end up being discredited and I find it hard to tell you about all the distress I have seen these ample-bosomed women suffering and I would prefer to hand over to the plastic surgeons.

Hips – now we are getting to the heart of the matter. Hips are what come immediately after the inflexion of the waist and ideally they start to form a guitar shape. This is an area where both maternity and femininity come together. Indeed, we talk about good 'child-bearing hips' and the wider the pelvis, the easier it is for babies to pass through. However, hips are no longer fashionable today and women who are blessed with them have trouble finding anything to wear. The current feminine ideal stipulates small, narrow hips in line with thighs and chest so that everything can be squeezed into unisex jeans. Hip bones must be protruding even though they risk knocking into those of your male partner.

Thighs. It is with thighs that the dictates become especially draconian; it is not about having just a little, you are not allowed anything at all any more. Here the dictate is aggressive to the point of being absurd. Without making distinctions, we can allow ourselves to use medical terms to describe these fleshy, quintessentially female contours.

Cellulite, or lipodystrophy, does indeed exist, resulting in massive and toxic infiltration of the tissues on hips, thighs, knees and ankles. Femininity is exaggerated to huge and serious proportions because of hormonal imbalance. I will look at this in greater detail in the next chapter.

Since I have written about it at length I am well acquainted with this problem.

But when describing natural shapes, who would dare take it upon themselves to raise this spectre? Who in such a casual way is confusing what is normal with what is pathological? You would need a good measure of perversity to try to make most women believe that they are more or less abnormal.

Men rarely read women's magazines but whenever they happen to inadvertently flick through the health and beauty sections they think they have stumbled across something written for Martians. Yet they would be alarmed to learn that their own wife thought she was suffering from a connective tissue disease that had to be treated urgently with all the most up-to-date medical and surgical methods. And they would be even more alarmed if they were to be shown this diseased organ.

To get back to our topic and to simplify things, let's say that current French canons for women deem that anything that can be found between a woman's skin and thigh muscles is abnormal which amounts to causing distress to 90 per cent of women.

Personal body odours. Before concluding this summary, I cannot stop myself from adding a few words about body odours. I have already mentioned the extent to which they are absolutely personal. Two identical human body odours do not exist, and our scent is perhaps the most personal thing we all possess. Desmond Morris points out that 'part of the process of forming a couple and falling in love implies a sort of olfactory imprinting, a fixation on the specific and individual odour of the partner's body'. Many other scientists are researching how well and how individually this chemical communication of ours works and they are drawing comparisons with our immune reactions.

If, as I believe, there is some truth in these statements, it would be the most amazing proof of our blindness to ignore or refuse to accept what is natural in us. As trivial as it may appear, if smell really does play its part in our becoming attached to the person we love, it would be utterly wrong to perpetuate the veto that incites us to sterilize our personal body odours.

However, I want to make sure that I have been properly understood because I am not advocating a lack of personal hygiene or that we neglect our bodies. A woman who gets out of a bath no longer smells of sweat or microbial multiplication, but, if she has been blessed by nature, she may still retain her natural fragrance. Sexual body odours are persistent and are meant to work this way.

What is injurious to a woman is the use of aggressive chemical deodorants to get rid of any last trace of her personal smell. At a time when most of us can have our appetites whetted by the whiff of a ripe Camembert or Stilton cheese, it is incomprehensible to me that we cannot tolerate these 'love fragrances'.

Finally, to finish off on an ironic note, you should be aware that most of the best-known perfumes, of which the French are the biggest consumers and exporters, contain 'diluted forms of products from sweat glands taken from other species of mammals that are not related to us'.

So, as far as body odours go, our current cultural edicts read like this: shave off anything that might smell, then dry out and neutralize with chemicals any smells that try to linger on, and finally spray yourself with products based on sexual secretions from other species.

Variations in the female body between individuals and races

I have briefly described to you the feminine ideal that currently holds sway in our Western societies. And one question immediately springs to mind: where can you find this woman in a million? Or, rather, who comes closest to it? The human genetic pool is so complex and diversified that the female body comes in a large number of individual and ethnic variations. All these combined determine the range of possibilities within which each culture selects canons for its role models.

Android bodies and gynoid bodies

The most typically feminine body is that of a gynoid woman.

This is the caricatured archetype of the Hottentot Venus, with a narrow bust, small shoulders and a wide pelvis that comes with voluminous thighs. Characteristically, it all gives an impression of the body opening out. When this body grows stout with age or through overeating, weight always goes on below the belly button, thereby accentuating the contrast between the upper and the lower body. This is the type of physique that tends to develop cellulite. As a rule, these women have a long and difficult puberty and irregular periods over a long time. Moreover, they systematically have an exaggerated curve of the lumbar spine and the foot arch drops. Sooner or later they will have problems with their circulation and they often suffer from varicose veins. They have low blood pressure, which means they are not very resilient, and they frequently succumb to all kinds of indispositions, dizzy spells and fainting. To sum up, these women are vulnerable, fragile and anxious.

The body of an android woman is the very opposite. The upper part is much sturdier, with a wide neck and broad shoulders, and a large bosom with a powerful chest that opens out. And then suddenly from below the belly button everything becomes unobtrusive, with an almost imperceptible waistline, boyish hips and small thighs on top of even more slender legs. When these women put on weight, it goes on their shoulders and back, their bosom turns into a bust worthy of a Fellini movie and their bras cut into their flesh from all angles. The stomach area becomes padded and the overall impression is one of an upside down triangle.

Generally, these women have a ruddy complexion with little veins on their nose and cheeks. When they reach the menopause, they tend to develop high blood pressure that 'runs in the family'.

Typically android women are robust, resilient, seldom soft and cuddly, and they burn up a lot of energy. They are if anything nervous, but rarely anxious. They have a natural need to be active. It is often said that they are masculine, which they find very upsetting. Statistically there are far fewer android women than gynoid women.

I have had to somewhat oversimplify the descriptions of these two types of female body, to make them clear and meaningful. In actual fact, in most women there is some combination of both tendencies and, as is usually the case, truth and harmony are found in the middle ground.

What we do need to remember from these two opposites is that women's curves are only one of the distinctive elements of femininity and they are found alongside other anatomical, physiological and even psychological characteristics. But of all these characteristics, women's curves remain the most expressive and reliable basic element.

As for men's tastes, we have to admit that most men tend to be attracted to the gynoid model; and that for curves to have been designed as they are, they absolutely have to belong on female territory.

Variations depending on race and ethnicity

The notion of race is one that has lost much of its scientific value and the three major categories – black, white or

Asian – no longer mean a great deal. We now talk about ethnic groups, which is far better.

So, as we cast our eyes around the planet, how do women's curves vary? I do not have the space I need to deal with a subject like this and it is not important to examine it in any great detail.

However, what does matter to me is to show you that as they evolved, certain ethnic groups have undergone mutations and because these groups have been geographically isolated this prevented their mutations from spreading. The most distinctive mutations can be seen in two African tribes that inhabit the same continent but are separated by several thousand kilometres. These two peoples alone embody the whole range of possible variations in the female body.

The Khoikhois and their female neighbours among the Bushmen in the Karahari desert have the very sort of body that Western women most detest. They have enormous thighs, with a volume and texture not seen anywhere else. And once these women put on weight, which is rare since they live on the edge of the desert, you see an extreme exaggeration of the gynoid body. What is particularly interesting to note is that this genetic feature occurs throughout the population; all the women are like this and have been like this for their husbands for hundreds of thousands of years. The husbands are always extremely amazed whenever they find themselves among foreign women as their bodies have a different shape. So we have to admit that if this mutation has managed to establish itself then most likely it must have been very much to the men's taste.

Masai women, who live in East Africa, represent the opposite pole. They are practically the only example of women who are so incredibly tall and slender. They are an extreme embodiment of what women in the West more or less dream of subconsciously. However, paradoxically, although the Masai women are slim they are not in fact bony as they have an exquisitely delicate skeleton, and what they lack in physical volume they make up for with their very shapely slenderness.

Finally, to make amends for any lack of generosity, nature has blessed Masai women with exceptionally fine-featured faces, which delight special correspondents reporting from Africa.

Without having to travel so far, we can find in our old Europe variations between ethnic groups that are just as clear cut. Since it has become easier for everyone to travel, we are able to see that in the West there are two major ethnic tendencies shaping women's bodies in different ways.

There is one tendency that in crude terms brings together Oriental and Mediterranean women. An Arab woman, a Lebanese woman and even a woman from North Africa all have a body that very clearly leans towards the gynoid, with pronounced curves. We know from her pelvis and thighs that a Spanish or an Italian woman, a woman from Nice or Greece is Mediterranean. It turns out that the hallmark stamped on the men from these ethnic groups is greater virility. They are hairier, smaller since their genitals are more sexually precocious, and they are more inclined to be possessive and view their women sexually. They develop behaviour patterns and cultures that champion the male–female bipolarity. For them, women's curves are a gift from heaven and they will put up very vigorous resistance to any archetypes that attempt to emaciate the female form.

Another tendency brings together the influence of Anglo-Saxon, Scandinavian and German cultures and by extension it has managed to some extent to spread to the United States. Here we find ourselves among taller women, with less gynoid bodies and firmer skin. Their curves are less apparent and more evenly proportioned.

The men are less assertive about their virility, their onset of puberty comes later, and although their sexual taboos are relaxed they seem less concerned about satisfying their libido.

It is curious to see that the geographical distribution of curves coincides with more precocious signs of sexuality and, ironically, with cultures in which there is greater sexual coercion. What is more, these two main tendencies occur in the south and in the north respectively, and if we allow ourselves to entertain plausible hypotheses, it is difficult to exclude the role weather may have played in producing these genetic differences.

The limits to normality and how men react to abnormal cases

The purpose of this book is to denounce the harm being done through this strange and artificial passion we have developed for thin and shapeless bodies. It is a plea for a return to the days when women's curves were celebrated.

However, I wish there to be absolutely no confusion whatsoever as you read this book; I am not hoping and praying for fat or obese women to rule the day. I am a nutritionist and I have already written several books flagging up the dangers of being overweight. Being downright and massively obese is an illness that short-ens life expectancy, especially as it comes with other risk factors, and it is quite legitimate to consider some-thing that can shorten your life span by a good few years as a dangerous thing.

However, I am going to make a confession that will come as quite a revelation to you. I consider our current taste for thinness and everything that is related cultur-ally to this trend as being far more dangerous. Not so much on a physiological level, since people rarely die of hunger as a result of chasing after these emaciating archetypes; but psychologically and sociologically it is a symptom of a society and culture that are disturbed.

And disturbed to the extent that they are making blun-ders so serious that they are impacting on their women's bodies and on what is most natural about them. A civilization that can go along with this sort of mutilation, whether consciously or not, is a civilization that is jeopardizing the cement sealing a bond that evolution has spent millions of years creating.

And this bond is the couple, the family, it is the men and women of tomorrow who face an uncertain future. I am saying that there is danger here not only for these curves that to you may seem trivial, and for these messenger smells that will have made you laugh, but there is danger because we are tampering too much with nature. Attacked from every side, like the last handful of brave warriors who would rather die than surrender, nature is likely to abandon us to our meltdown.

Having said this, as much as we deem women's curves to be natural, what are their limits and when do they start to actually become abnormal?

I will answer as a biologist: there are three sets of very specific circumstances that put the individual or species under threat:

- Firstly, when they prevent a woman from carrying out everyday activities.
- Secondly, when they threaten to shorten a woman's life span through symptoms of plethora which may be associated with them.
- Thirdly, when they start to fill most men with repulsion.

The first two sets of circumstances are so obvious and so easy to distinguish that they raise no objections at all. As for the third, I can tell you all you want to hear as this forms part of my work. I see obese women on a regular basis, sometimes extremely obese women who have trouble squashing themselves into the lift to come up to my surgery. I also see women who are so skinny they come for consultations. What always strikes me is that my obese patients hardly ever have sexual problems. However enormous these women may be, their husbands might complain, get annoyed and even at times space out sexual intercourse but they never stop it altogether. I have seen women who weigh one hundred and fifty kilos, over twenty-three stone, who have problems dressing and moving around but who manage to achieve the feat of a daily orgasm.

Being extremely thin is much less successful in the bedroom, and as paradoxical as it may seem, these women go humbly seeking their pleasure in vain.

I realize that you will find it hard to believe me and I was just as surprised myself, but this is what I observe day in, day out and I have come to accept it as such. I have known some women who because they are ashamed of their bodies will not allow themselves any sexual relations. If anyone were to look upon their rolls of fat, they would feel as if they were being seared with a hot iron. These women often bring their husbands along to consultations, and if the husbands are keen for them to lose weight then it is often with the clearly avowed intention of retrieving their partner's body.

I know of cases, few and far between of course, of African and Oriental communities where men who are rich and powerful literally force-feed their wives, turning them into really experimentally obese women. Do not worry; these are not groups of cannibals, but rather men who have a bizarre passion for female fat and bulk.

In *Amarcord*, a wonderful Fellini film, there is one Dionysian and possibly autobiographical scene, where a young teenager full of sexual desire is enthralled and mesmerized by the tobacconist's ample body. Lifting up this mere scrap of a teenage boy, the tobacconist envelops him in her bosom as the atmosphere evokes the end of the world and a return to the maternal womb. In another equally famous film, Ingmar Bergman's *Cries and Whispers*, a young woman who knows she is going to die awaits her fate and in a similar way reacts by returning to the source of life as she clings on hysterically to her maid's ample, resplendent body.

Both examples confirm that in men's universal collective subconscious, excessive overabundance of the female body shape is an archetype for life and plenitude. You may find this strange, but our subconscious makes a straight choice between two alternatives: ample flesh pulsates with life whereas thinness spells out phoney.

I also see patients who are thin; far fewer since fashion has been permanently awarding thinness full marks. However, genuinely thin women sense somewhere that they are being duped, and what for healthy women is an unspoken dream is for these women a biological nightmare. Apart from the problems examined in the chapter dealing with deliberate weight loss carried to excess, thinness always jeopardizes sexual relations.

When wearing loose-fitting clothes, very thin women can create the illusion of having curves, but they systematically lose all their lovers as soon as their final piece of camouflage falls away. I still remember how the confessions of one of my former patients left me feeling most uneasy.

At first sight, this woman appeared very thin. Once she removed her clothes, she was all bones and seemed malnourished. I thought she had come to ask me for help in regaining some pounds so I was shocked once she made it clear that she wanted to lose even more weight.

Yet she was an intelligent woman and I could talk to her. She told me that she had tried everything possible to gain weight but to no avail. She was constitutionally thin and all her attempts had ended in failure. She then noticed that there was a rare category of sexually disturbed men she could attract if she became impossibly thin. She told me about her experiences and even today I still feel a strange discomfort when thinking about her pitiful sexuality.

She confessed to me, and I can hardly bring myself to write it down, that at times she would resist the temptation of eating for more than three days so that she could look her best when meeting up with a lover. She blocked all the arguments I used with her, always countering with this one reply: 'No normal man wants anything to do with me, all I have left are a few perverts and since I am unable to put on any weight then help me to lose a bit more.'

I referred this woman to a neuro-psychiatric psycho-analyst, who wrote a very interesting study about her but he never managed to get her to change her mind.

Fortunately, cases like this are extremely rare and confirm that acute thinness repels sexual desire. I do not know whether I will end up persuading you that men do prefer women with curves but I can assure you that most men recoil from women who have none.

Women's curves through the ages

I have been talking to you about our current canons and what we deem suitable for appreciation in women today. You must have picked up how much I totally disagree with these dictates. However, you still only know some of my arguments.

I would now like to point out a fact that to my mind is fundamental. As far back into the past as we are able to look there has never been any fad for thinness that is remotely akin to what we are subjecting ourselves to at present. We are not the rule, we are the exception. And since we are behaving in such an unusual way, this really ought to set our minds thinking. Man has been around for a couple of million years and at all times and in all places female beauty has been associated with fullness and curves. And yet for the past couple of generations, with all the arrogance that comes with being the latest ones on the scene, we have turned our noses up at what every single generation before us has found entrancing.

I have no doubt that there will be some experts among you who will raise objections, pointing to cultural records in our possession, such as Egyptian statues on bas-reliefs depicting rather slender, thin women. And pointing out that some Madonnas from the Middle Ages look nothing like a callipygian Venus. I quite agree; however, by pre-empting these objections, I intend to counter them. Egyptian and medieval art are the prototypes of an art that was essentially religious and commissioned entirely by those who supported what was deemed at that period to be sacred. To hold up an image of a goddess or a Madonna laden with appealing signs of active sexuality would have been unseemly and might well have led to the stake or the grave.

However, let's not get ahead of ourselves. I realize, because this is what I am concerned with, that it is difficult for us to even imagine that we are the first generation of humankind to have constructed an idealized model of thinness. Whenever I state that men love women with curves, I see quite plainly that I am somewhat scandalizing the very women who ought to be giving me most encouragement. Our cultural blindness is such that I could be easily accused of having a taste for the paradoxical. However, if there is a paradox to be found anywhere, it lies more in the gigantic disparity between the ninety thousand generations that have held curves in adulation and our pitiful, tiny generation, isolated and insolent, that professes a dangerous and decadent penchant for thinness.

If you still have any doubts about this, you have not been well enough informed.

The first prehistoric men

These men and women could not write but they could draw and paint. Altamira and Lascaux provide marvellous, authentic examples of this universal art. Many experts tell us that their stylistic form does not prevent us from recognizing the animal species they drew so skilfully. In these cave paintings, there are very few examples of men. A few hunters are depicted moving and carrying weapons of the period but there is very little detail about their bodies. On the other hand, women are depicted far more frequently and here the message comes across loud and clear. It is not their curves that are all-important but their size. These female bodies are so large, so stout and so heavy that we cannot help but see in them a symbol of fecundity. Their corpulence borders on enormity; the pelvis and thighs give the body a diamond shape. There are a few very small statuettes still extant, made of horn or bone, which fit inside a hand. You only need to have clutched one of these statuettes once in your palm to understand what these first men must have fantasized about. However, you will tell me that these people were so primitive that it is a good thing we have changed our tastes and customs.

I am not so sure about this. These first men were as nature made them. Their culture was rudimentary or almost non-existent. So their message is definitely as pure as it gets and the one that comes closest to our basic biological hardwiring. If a man from this period showed through his art that he venerated women's curves to the extent that they were so exaggerated, then this definitely had nothing to do with satisfying the needs of some fleeting fad; rather he was giving voice to his deepest nature, albeit a crude and perhaps unrefined one.

To persuade you of this, just think about the time these men must have devoted to hunting to be able to feed these women until they were plump and to their taste.

Present-day primitive tribes

Ethnologists have more or less recorded every single primitive tribe that is still living today. The diversity of these groups of humans, spread out across several continents, reveals great genetic and cultural differences. Being totally isolated for thousands of years has enabled complex mutations to take place which prevent us from making any comparisons as regards the morphology of the female body. However, as far as I am aware there is no primitive tribe that culturally demands its women to be thin. As a rule, they stick with what nature has shaped, more or less generously depending on the latitude and what is available to eat.

It is obvious that most of these populations are on the verge of extinction. They hunt and lead nomadic lives, making it difficult for their women to become corpulent. We should take note of a clue likely to be of interest to us – the wives of chiefs and important men are often more corpulent than the other women. However, as they get more to eat this argument is insufficient.

On the other hand, in the art and graphic representations of these peoples, time and again we come across stylized fertility symbols that are strangely reminiscent of those of the first men.

From this brief look at ethnology we can see that primitive tribes respect the shapes with which nature has endowed them but that some fantasies of female fullness and opulence, projected into their artistic representations, tell us more about their aspirations than their reality. So ideally these tribes still aspire to women with curves and these curves are an outward sign of wealth.

The Orient, cradle of civilizations

I have no intention of systematically delving into all the cultures that appeared along with the first civilizations. That is not what we are about. Women probably discovered agriculture as they stayed at home and unwittingly observed what happened to seeds. Rearing cattle was left to the hunters; they must have forgotten to slaughter some young wild animals that were still feeding from their mothers and then been surprised to discover how they were gradually able to domesticate them. Both innovations allowed man to settle in one place and no longer be dependent on hunting.

This is when the first expressions of art emerged in Assur, Elam, Nineveh, Babylon, Thebes and Carnac. This amazing birth of culture took place across an area hardly bigger than France where two great ethnic trends, the Semitic and the Indo-European, converged, fought and at times merged together.

The violence and energy that man had once expended on hunting seems to have been transferred to permanent warmongering. However, sheltered from danger, far from the fields that needed tending and animals that needed watching, the artist and the priest now appeared on the scene.

At this period, an artist was not free. His role was to glorify chiefs and kings through his works and to serve a priesthood that needed images to impose its gods.

As stories of battles were being related and deities were being shaped, what became of women and their bodies? Obviously they were relegated to a minor position. Everywhere man had taken power and he was even in control of figurative representation. However, alongside great monumental and glorious works we do find scenes of everyday life and it is quite apparent, especially for fundamentally Semitic civilizations, that their ideal was still women with curves.

All these cruel and savage wars saw kings' heads fall time and again and the same scenario always ensued. Hordes of Barbarians with fresh, new blood would come and destroy civilizations that had grown decrepit and weakened by their comfort and wealth.

Then as two ogres appeared, the Persians and the Egyptians, everything returned to normal again and, having swallowed up all the other warring factions, they divided up the lands. This spelt the end of the Semitic civilizations' temporal greatness.

The Persians were the Indo-European avant-garde. Their women are less gynoid, yet their Semitic slaves must have ended up giving the Persians a liking for voluptuous curves as their art depicts plump women.

The Egyptians present us with a problem, because a severe, hierarchical rigidity permeates their art. Most of the women portrayed are goddesses and they rarely have curves. However, this absence of curves is significant because if the goddess of death has none then this is because she is terrifying.

The purpose behind all these depictions of female gods was to impress the masses; they were there to inspire fear, respect, idolatry, trust – but under no circumstances were they meant to awaken sexual desire. The priests were adamant about this. In the true sense, these goddesses had to be disembodied; in other words, the statues had to shed their flesh. So this makes it difficult for us to know precisely what the Egyptians liked.

The female musicians depicted in the tomb of Djeserkareseneb were not there for kings, or queens or priests. They decorate the tomb of an artist who must have created them during his lifetime to convince himself of the attractions of the afterlife. There is no sign here of conventional rigidity and we can see one dancer and four female musicians whose beauty and grace make these few centimetres of plaster one of the world's artistic wonders. I do not know if the young women depicted can tell us about three to four thousand years of culture and fashion on their own, but it is abundantly apparent that these bodies appear to be pulsating with life. Myself, I find them shapely and curvaceous, with probably the healthiest shapeliness I know. Here there is no unnecessary or burdensome volume; the bodies are slender, supple, delicate and graceful but with well-defined breasts and round yet light hips and thighs. These shapes are so pure and beautiful that we are moved to wonder if they ever existed or if they were not instead the artist's invention, reflecting a universal aspiration.

Ancient Greece and the definitive canons for beauty

Greece was populated through successive invasions which placed its original indigenous population in the background. The Indo-Europeans were still at work here and then without any warning the miracle happened. Before them, there had been chaos, war and anarchy when strength and fear alone gave some cohesion to all the empires that fell in succession.

Four centuries before Jesus Christ, it was the Greeks who had already laid the foundations for democracy and tragic drama, who had brought forth the most wonderful architectural creations that the world will ever see and, most importantly – and perhaps with more brilliance than anywhere else – they created a statuary whose perfection we have never managed to rival. But in doing so, and this is what is of interest to us, they defined once and for all the notion of harmony in the human body. If we look closely at what Phidias or Praxiteles achieved, it is as if nature, in a moment of distraction, had revealed to them her recipe for universal harmony.

The frescoes at the Parthenon, the *Venus de Milo* and the *Aphrodite* of Cnidus show us the Greek canons for beauty. These canons had a strange destiny. Political Greece would disappear, dominated by other empires, but the Greek archetype would remain and all the conquerors who in turn invaded Greece were themselves colonized from the inside and could not help but see the world through Greek eyes. Today, the canons of Phidias still remain our basic criteria. Any artist who goes through art school is imbued with this vision. If, carried away by a taste for something new and different, an artist creates very different shapes and proportions, they will still keep in mind a system of references. For all figurative artists, this Greek harmony is their compass.

And four centuries before our era began, how did the citizens of Athens view the female body? It is difficult to describe this model as it represents absolute equilibrium. The breasts are shapely but never heavy, the waistline is distinct but not pronounced, the hips are well delineated but simply offset the hollow of the waistline. The thighs are rounded, without losing their shape or becoming excessive. Together they give the impression of an overall structure where the various parts come together to form a whole. This is Greek beauty, the incarnation of feminine purity.

So it is interesting to find out from these demigods, these inspired artists, what they thought about women's curves. Curves are everywhere so we know they loved them – but in their own way, which means without exaggeration and without ever violating the ideal proportions. Irrefutable proof that their formula for beauty included being shapely and curvaceous is that unfortunately no woman today would want to look like a Venus from this period.

For a very long time now, on my desk I have had a photograph of a big-bottomed Mexican woman and one of the *Venus de Milo*. They are displayed quite openly so that patients can take a look at them without being indiscreet. I find the way women react to these two different types of morphology extremely interesting. I have never seen any woman who has not recoiled at the gynoid Mexican woman.

The *Venus de Milo* elicits very different and far more complex reactions. She emanates an impression of immediate harmony and does this regardless of cultural and social status. The Greeks' greatness, and their secret, was to have discovered the combination that opened the doors to beauty in every man and every woman. And yet, this abstract appreciation of her beauty does not lead to any desire to look like her and most women find her old-fashioned.

Men react very differently. They show that they are better able to ignore our cultural dictates. Often I get a rather raunchy reaction when they look at the Mexican woman. However, if I ask them to say a little more about what they think of her, they get embarrassed. Faced with a photo of this extremely gynoid statue I can sense their ambivalence as they delight in imagining what such ample volumes might feel like while struggling with the effect of cultural pressures which decree that it is difficult to be seen with this sort of woman.

I have to admit that although the men agree that the Greek statue is superb, few of them admit to being sexually inspired by her.

I have thought a lot about the different ways men and women see these photos and they illustrate perfectly how the female body and its curves are not meant to get women excited. The message is addressed to the men. So if women are starting to open our mail, can they please do so without trying to denigrate it. If tomorrow there were no more mirrors, men would not be very different. Women, on the other hand, would regain much of their self-confidence and with it their attractiveness.

Among all these inner workings, the only reaction I cannot comprehend is the kind of sexual indifference the men show towards the *Venus de Milo*. She radiates such harmony that it turns her into something abstract, which, in all likelihood, makes it difficult for them to see what is a model of equilibrium as a sexual being.

So with their statues, the Greeks have confirmed that they too preferred women with curves and that these curves are inseparable from femininity. However, their art was far more than a mere reflection of the tastes of that period. It ended up establishing itself as the absolute, classical benchmark for beauty. Because they were such aesthetes, what the Greeks have to say is worth far more than what other civilizations could tell me.

How the Romans saw women's curves

In world history, the Romans have distinguished themselves as the prototype of the invader and legislator. As legislators, they have passed on to us their idea of law, on which the Western system is based. As invaders, they swallowed up everything they conquered by the sword. Greek art was the only booty that stuck in their throats. And Greek art was the only artistic beacon the Romans followed passionately until their decline. Accordingly, as we would expect, we find that their cultural canons on female beauty are modelled exactly on those of Athens. Women's curves therefore remained fashionable, enhancing the bodies of women in Rome. This is of great interest to us, since it was the Romans who passed on to us some of our Latin character, grafting it on to a substructure of Gallic impetuosity. Rome was a great crossroads that opened out on to the Western world. Rome's domination of the world for five centuries changed nothing about the way women's curves were viewed and they retained their place in men's hearts.

The Middle Ages

The Middle Ages began with the fall of Rome, and finished with the Italian Renaissance. As far as women's curves are concerned, this was a period of obscurity. Paganism gave way to triumphant Catholicism and with it a re-emergence of sexual taboos. All art was commissioned by an austere clergy so it did not dare go against the interdictions.

Consequently, no graphic or pictorial creation ventured to show a naked female body. Or, if it did, infinite care was taken to avoid any temptation that might be deemed erotic. Women's curves were handled as if they were some dangerous explosive.

To understand what people prized in these dark ages, we do better to go to the lay people or even better the warlords: violent and bawdy, inveterate hunters and womanizers. Their reply is straightforward and unambiguous – only curves receive their blessing; their wives might well be skinny but their mistresses never.

The Middle Ages had two different ways of viewing women's curves: a holy language that saw them as temptation from the devil, which proves that it was missing the mark; and a profane language that, by hanging on to common sense, could instead see the hand of God at work and as such revered them.

The Italian Renaissance

The Middle Ages came to an end because of their austerity and obscurantism. There was a return to the song and laughter of Italy and now my argument becomes all too easy. From Botticelli to Michelangelo, flesh reappears in all its sublimity; the wealth available gave these artists an unhoped-for opportunity to show off their talents. How could we possibly imagine these effusive, dynamic geniuses selecting their models among the period's skin-and-bone pariahs? This century is all about opulence of shape, colour and light. The flesh is weak but it is also full and firm. Although she is clothed and only showing the top half of her body, we must surely imagine that the Mona Lisa was full-bodied. With Raphael's grace, Madonnas managed to remain virginal despite their curves, which are no longer absent from religious paintings.

The Renaissance, genius and women's curves are but one.

Modern Europe

Already two million years of prehistory and forty-five centuries of history have passed before our eyes and still no categorical denial. No fashion, no culture that has gone before us has ever dared to conceive and create an ideal of thinness or attempt such a distortion of shape.

Must I keep on bombarding you with evidence which you are perhaps well aware of but which you may not always have in mind when that size 10 no longer fits and you have to resign yourself to a size 12? So as not to tire you out, I will take a shortcut through the final few centuries that separate us from the great schism of thinness. And to spice up my argument I will stick to the most wonderful examples of artists who were madly in love with full bodies and women's curves.

Rembrandt was Dutch, as were his most beautiful models, even if he managed to conceal their identity behind biblical names. That his Bathsheba exudes abundance comes as no surprise. He even succumbed to the temptation of painting full faces. Take a look at his works in the Louvre and you will see that one of the world's greatest artists had none of our obsession for shrinking body mass.

Rubens was also Dutch and an international court painter. It is said that he received so many commissions that he did not paint all his pictures himself. He would come along at the end and add the final few strokes that made the flesh radiant and come alive. I hardly dare talk about what he painted. To speak up for his view of the female form is nowadays deemed as practically indecent. As fat takes over there is no shape left. Here perhaps we can even see obesity, but a resplendent obesity that does not hide itself away; it spreads everywhere, even devouring the light and the colours. There are only three centuries between him and us and every museum vies to display his works.

The kings of this period, the chief dignitaries in all the courts, paid an exorbitant price to display this flesh on their walls and live with it constantly under their eyes.

It is hard to believe, but this is how it was. Rubens was the greatest European apologist for the triumph of fat, along with all the other people who exercised some influence during the seventeenth century when he was painting. So all you full-figured women reading this book, do not weep and think there is something wrong with you; you were simply born into the wrong century, or even the wrong quarter- or wrong half-century as far as your anatomy is concerned. But do not despair. Sixty centuries of history have their eyes on you and do not see your situation as hopeless at all.

Rubens died rich and was greatly mourned. He left behind him a body of work that has made a name for him across the centuries. With regret, he left behind him a European culture insatiable for pleasure and men greedy for full-bodied women.

The Impressionists

With the Impressionists came the final great change in direction before modern art appeared. Their revolutionary approach was to use light and to paint outdoors. As for their models, they simply chose the women of their time. So again there are no surprises here: generous bosoms and hips that are occasionally emphasized by baskets – all done with the flurry and energy of natural, bright, sunny colours.

Manet's *Déjeuner sur l'herbe*, which is now on display in the Musée d'Orsay Paris, takes up a whole section of wall on the first floor. As I live nearby I often go and take a stroll through the gallery. And I am always surprised to see that this painting, which at the time created quite a scandal, continues to shock the people looking at it today. What was provocative when it was painted was that the lady at the picnic was completely naked, bathed in an unusual light but surrounded by fully dressed men.

Nowadays, it is only the fullness of her body and her curves that raise a smile or make people feel uncomfortable. Now and then I mingle with the visitors who stop for a moment to look at this compelling painting.

There is usually a reaction among young women, mostly students, who have trouble comprehending how women of this sort could have been attractive.

One day one of these young female students on a group tour said to me, 'What a strange period. The men weren't exactly spoilt back then, perhaps this Manet chap had a particular thing for that sort of woman.'

'That isn't how I see it – these painters showed us what they saw around them. The only one who was perhaps a bit obsessed with firm, young flesh was Renoir; he was a master at painting pearly skin and the bodies of redheads.'

'Yes, I saw that downstairs. The overall result is amazing but his model, his servant or his niece, they're really grotesque – why didn't he paint normal women?'

We stopped there as otherwise we would have got into too much of a discussion. I watched her return to the group and looked at her body. She was a young girl just like so many nowadays: slim, tall and quite shapeless. She joined the other girls and boys of her age and from a distance I thought they all looked very much alike. They were dressed in the same jeans, the same footwear, the same shirts and polo shirts. Their hair was shoulder-length and hardly styled. And I understood her reaction. She must have been about twenty years old and, for at least ten years since starting to turn into a woman, she must have heard, all quite subconsciously, the main messages conveyed by our culture. She will have seen older girls wearing trousers and read women's magazines where mythical models strut around, all tanned and bony, on tropical beaches to increase bikini sales. Film stars who are idolized, adverts for mineral water to help with dieting, and even the heroines in cartoons all look as flat as a board.

How could this sort of message ever be doubted when you feel its strength, when it is all around you and constantly reiterated and you are so young, innocent and malleable!

Perhaps it was on that very day, in front of the *Déjeuner sur l'herbe*, once so scandalous because of its nudity and then for its model's curves, that the idea of writing this book came to me. I have one very small wish among many, and that is for this young girl to read my book as she is bound to recognize herself if she does.

Renoir died in 1919. The century had already gone through a world war. He was an old man suffering from rheumatism, refusing to give in even though his deformed fingers caused him pain as he furiously painted these female shapes that he perhaps sensed were about to fall out of favour. He never tried to 'airbrush' his models. Quite the opposite. He is famous the world over; with his death nothing has changed – there are still men out there who love women's curves.

Maillol

Since we are in the Louvre let's stay there. Or rather let's go outside through the Tuileries gardens and walk the three hundred metres that take us away from the square outside the Louvre. We go down the rue de Rivoli, leaving behind the statue of Jeanne d'Arc on horseback on the left as we go right and walk down towards the river. There, on both sides, mounted on plinths and appearing to emerge out of the grass, are six or seven amazing sculptures which France has chosen to honour one of its greatest artists – Maillol.

I would love to know who decided to choose them for this permanent exhibition which I hope will always stay here. I would personally like to thank the unknown person responsible. If it were Malraux, I would be delighted that this posthumous homage is given to someone I have always held in great esteem.

Every day hundreds of buses, taxis and cars pass by the reassuring sight of these bronze statues which are full of shape and life. My feeling of pleasure stops when I think about all the women looking at the sculptures, as I know all too well how they will react. I have talked so often about the statues to women who are cultured and sophisticated and to those less educated, and common sense was lacking every time. 'It's beautiful but it's ugly. In itself it's beautiful but for what it is, it's ugly.'

'If I looked like that I'd never be seen on a beach.' Once, out of curiosity, I went along to see an exhibition of Doucet's paintings in a Parisian art gallery and I had the good fortune to bump into the model who had inspired Maillol. After I had been round the show, I came face to face with the gallery manager, who asked me what I thought of the exhibition. We started talking about art and quite innocently she asked me if I liked Maillol's statues, the very ones I have just described. You can imagine my response. Then with a wide, radiant smile she confessed to me: 'But do you know who the model was for these statues?'

I could not answer so she said, 'But it was me, Dina Vierny. I had great difficulty holding all those uncomfortable positions.'

And as I looked at her in amazement she continued, 'Yes, I know, you must be surprised, I've changed quite a lot since then. But I am his sole legatee and can authenticate all his works. I know them all by heart. It takes a long to time to shape a statue, you know!'

It always makes an impression on you when you meet the living model for works of art that you imagine came out of some other creative place. But it is also reassuring. I never saw her again but for a long time I greeted her every time I drove past those statues.

I will finish my inventory with Maillol as we have come to the eve of the Second World War. From 1939 to 1945, men from all corners of the world came to Europe to fight. Whatever the uniform they wore, the soldiers brought with them a picture of their sweetheart and it's a safe bet that these men still loved their women with curves.

6. Consequences of the thin vs curves conflict

Having analyzed women's natural curves, I want to reiterate once again, so that there is no confusion in your minds, that being shaped this way has nothing to do with weight or being overweight. Bingeing and how we eat can only make us obese; it can never produce curvaceous women. Hormones and being female produce curves and fullness of flesh, and if these curves did not exist a woman's body would be entirely neutral, making it difficult to differentiate between the sexes.

If you want any further, conclusive proof, I can tell you about the male transvestites I sometimes examine. Driven by their fantastical desire to take on a gender that nature has not bestowed upon them, some have no hesitation whatsoever in taking high doses of oestrogens, and oestrogen is the most female hormone you can get. And do you know what happens to them? Their bodies change. Within a few weeks their breasts have started to fill out and at the same time their hips and thighs become padded. And, as surprising as this may appear to you, the characteristic, biological signs of female curves get tacked on to their former masculine silhouette. Could there be more persuasive proof than this of the purely sexual nature of these curves? Who can provide me with any other reason for such a radical metamorphosis?

I will repeat this one last time: these anatomical features have a single purpose, but a very significant one, and this is to underline our differences and to allow both poles, male and female, to recognize each other and become attracted to one another; the reproduction of the species being the ultimate purpose of this understanding.

I have endeavoured to show you that we are the first and only generation of humankind that has wanted to tamper with this finely-tuned mechanism, which nature has tried and tested on every living creature.

Human beings are very adaptable – it is said to be what characterizes our species and what has enabled us to be prodigiously successful, so much more so than all the other species with which we share the planet. I agree with this. However, will we manage to go on preserving our sexual and emotional bond if we are forever chipping away at these differences? Personally, my answer is no and I will tell you why.

The consequences of this conflict are grave and go far beyond what is happening to women's curves. If we take a closer look, whenever we attempt to lessen the differences between men and women, we do not just stop at body shape but – and this is perhaps even more serious – we try to alter our respective behaviour patterns and roles. When women are forced to work, to be more aggressive and make more demands, then the differences begin to fade away once more. When women are encouraged to take less interest in their homes and devote less time to their children, the gap grows ever smaller. And if, for their part, men lose their self-assurance and virility and their desire to be protective, we will all probably finish up being so similar that I am not convinced we will still feel as inclined to form pairs.

Common sense tells us that *opposites attract* and biologists confirm this unreservedly. What will happen if we lose everything that sets us apart and makes the sexes different? There will no longer be a positive and a negative pole, there will only be vague, neutral poles that have no reason any longer to be attracted to one another.

However, let's come back to women's curves. It is clear that at present they are no longer fashionable. This is not an opinion, it is a statement of fact and I do not think anyone will contradict me on this point. So I would like to ask a simple question: what is to happen to all the women who do not conform to this cultural dictate? Has a machine been invented for this purpose, which will smooth away women's curves? Not as far as I am aware.

So what do we suggest they do – these women who are growing impatient at not fitting in with the norm? We take them for a ride by offering them miracle creams and, if we are a little more serious, we advise them to see a doctor! And I am one of the doctors working in nutrition who knows how to treat obese patients or those who, as womanly as they may look, are on the verge of distorting their shape. However, when it comes to perfectly healthy, normal and I would go as far as to say blessed women, what answer is there for them? If you venture to suggest that there is nothing wrong with them, that it is all in their imagination and that essentially they have been poisoned by cultural brainwashing, they are likely to see you as a bad doctor or at the very least an old fogey who is out of step with the times. This in itself is not serious, but it does not get us anywhere.

And these women, who feel lost, inevitably end up clutching on to the line of thought that losing weight is the only way to change their body shape. Losing weight will make me lose body volume and, sooner or later, I'll lose my thighs, my hips and breasts. I have to tell you that it is later rather than sooner. My teacher Marcel Zara, now dead, was a doctor at the end of the Second World War and had the dreadful task of inspecting the Nazi death camps. He told me how he had seen women shaved, starved and who had wasted away as far as is humanly possible, yet they still had a slight roundness; the only sign that helped him identify them as women. I can also tell you that he found the same feature in women who had died of hunger. So if you hate your body shape, losing weight is not a solution. It would be so much simpler to just *adjust* the taboo a little.

I do not intend to pursue this any further, despite being driven by my passion and desire to persuade. There is a ban on women's curves and there are women with curves. Lots of women with curves. I would even say that apart from a few rare exceptions there are practically *only* women with curves. This dilemma, this opposition between nature and culture, leads to repercussions and disturbances that affect men just as much as women and which is what we will look at in this chapter.

Frustrated urges cause neurosis in animals

Man's sexual instinct is programmed to perceive, be moved by and to react to a woman's curves. Yet nowadays everything conspires to discredit and even invert the sexual value of this message. How will men react? Certain biologists have tried to find this out with experiments on animals and their results reveal very serious neurotic disturbances. But read on and you will see for yourselves.

B.F. Skinner, an eminent American psychologist, made a name for himself as a public enemy of rats and pigeons. He invented a sort of cage, the Skinner box, into which an impressive number of gadgets can be introduced, so that the animal can be conditioned through reward or punishment. The reward is food; the punishment is often an electric shock. Using this method, he was able to train rats to perform all sorts of tasks for which nature had not equipped them.

This same school of psychology has attempted to verify what would happen if an animal instinct was pitted against the electric punishment method. Two major instincts were studied this way – the sexual instinct and the feeding instinct.

Rats are rodents and well deserve their reputation since they are animals that easily and frequently indulge their sexual urges. Imagine a male rat on one side of a cage and a female on the other side. A barrier runs across the middle that can be electrified whenever desired. A rat, deprived of his female for quite some time, will run towards her but encounters this barrier. As he stands up against this unwelcome partition a weak current is passed through it. Our rat, which can smell his female, does not pay attention to the current; he does not even notice it. And then the intensity is gradually increased. There comes a point at which this poor animal will give up and return to its sad half of the cage.

If the female rat is on heat and if the isolation continues, the male will make another attempt and resist very painful intensities but in the end he is forced to give up.

However, mind does try to win over body. And if this little game goes on for a long time, there will be a very intense internal conflict between the rat's sexual instinct and the punishing shock. This conflict will plunge the male rat into a neurotic state which oddly enough is very similar to what can happen to human beings. The rat will remain in the corner of his cage, will no longer show any interest in anything, he will stop eating and gradually let himself die.

The same results are obtained when the rat becomes accustomed to getting its food by pushing a lever. Once the rat has been well trained, the lever is cruelly reversed so that with each attempt to feed itself the rat ends up with an electric shock. Conflict in the rat becomes rapidly apparent and neurosis follows.

This is a general rule which unfortunately has been confirmed with a great number of species. Any attempt to frustrate an instinct leads to a refusal to live, which manifests itself at the outset through signs of neurosis.

Can any conclusion be drawn from these cruel experiments that could shed light on our topic? I think so.

When we disparage women's curves, we are not really preventing our sexuality from expressing itself or being satisfied, so the conditions of this experiment are not being exactly replicated. However, we are taking a step towards extinguishing one of the signals that controls our sexuality. It is a minor assault but an assault nonetheless. It takes very little to modify instinctive behaviour. A few electric shocks and an oversexed rat loses all desire to copulate or eat.

If a large blue mark is painted on to a female lizard to make her look like a male and the disguised female is placed before a real male lizard, the mere sight of the intruder infuriates him to the point where he makes to pounce on the interloper and bite it. However, suddenly at the very last moment he smells the powerful odour of the disguised female, detects that something is wrong and is no longer able to attack. Now he is worried, uncertain about what to do, sniffing and peering at this big blue mark. Conflict arises in his little primitive brain and it will forever disturb his sexuality and his aggressiveness. He will never again be the same aggressive male. He will be forever frustrated, a little like a dog that, beaten for no good reason when a puppy, will waver when called, torn between its desire to go bounding up and an old, deep-rooted fear of getting hit.

We are now getting much closer to our topic. Here is a lizard that no longer has a clue about which way to turn and whose sexuality can no longer find its signs of attraction, and this is what present-day man would be like if, by waving a magic wand, we could grant all these women what they want. Fortunately for us, when nature hardwires us with a sign for sexual recognition, she chooses one that is difficult to eradicate. A little as if nature had somehow foreseen that one day we would be tempted to try to do without the sign. So women are not yet out of the woods and until the day they are, they will suffer the consequences of the conflict arising from having something they no longer want. We will now take a look at these psychological and physiological consequences.

Psychological disturbances caused by having curves

The difficulty of finding something to wear

There are three main reasons why we wear clothes – for comfort, modesty and decoration.

By comfort I mean that we cover ourselves up according to the temperature outside. In winter we dress warmly and in summer we wear something light.

For reasons of modesty, here things start to become a little more complex. Our bodies are made up of shapes and parts that we all know are there. They are so obvious that we do not pay them any attention but they do have a meaning and they carry messages. The messages from a female body speak more or less this language: 'I am a woman' or 'I have been pubescent for some time now so I can copulate'. And if these signals come from parts of the body that are very harmonious and expressive, they will as a rule trigger the temptation to get closer until contact is made.

Women's curves are the most direct elements in this type of instinctive communication but not always the best known. We live in society and what we like to show our partners is not always good to display to other men. You do not usually talk to people you don't know, and even less so using this sort of language which is so direct. So it is absolutely essential to hide these elements away by placing a screen between your body and the eyes of all these strangers scuttling around like ants in our city streets. Imagine for a moment what twenty minutes on the underground at rush hour would be like if we were not wearing clothes. I can barely bring myself to think about it.

However, you will point out to me that some women's clothes only just cover the skin and reveal a very precise outline of the body's contours. In this particular instance, I will concede that garments of this sort are only doing a small part of their job as they show off to better advantage what they are meant to be concealing. Have you not seen a young woman, in the spring or summer months, wearing a tightly fitting T-shirt over a taut bosom with no bra? The most expressive sign of attraction is the outline of her nipple protruding through the cotton. Now ask a man to have a serious conversation with a woman sending out signs like these. All it takes are two tiny, barely noticeable nipples and even the chastest man is unable to avert his gaze entirely. Is it possible to avoid signs of this sort permanently?

So a woman in clothes conveys a double language – 'don't look but you can still see'.

Some sociologists believe that the reason for this ambiguity stems from the fact that in going about her daily life a woman uses ways of being attractive to lessen male hostility. Women are vulnerable and, in the anonymous world in which we live, if she did not make it so obvious that she is a woman, she would rarely be given an easy time. A woman who stalls her car at a busy junction would have violent abuse hurled at her if her long, blonde hair was not there to temper the aggression a blunder of this sort might otherwise unleash.

Who among you male readers has not felt ashamed at watching some unknown, unaccompanied woman struggle with a suitcase that is too heavy for her? But let's not go off on too many tangents. Women's clothing plays an anti-sexual role but nonetheless it protects her identity.

Lastly, the third role of clothes is to be decorative. And because of this, clothes are bound to be part of fashion and forever changing. Now we are moving away from what is universal to touch on what is individual and cultural. If everywhere people dress to protect themselves from bad weather, they do not dress the same way everywhere.

There was a time when women made their own clothes. They could create the garments they liked and make their patterns fit their shape and style. Nowadays, economic conditions have changed completely and this sort of individual dressmaking has more or less disappeared. Women no longer have time for it and, besides, they can easily find ready-to-wear clothing which manufacturers are able to produce better than they can.

However, by dressing this way, women are being forced to lose some part of their personality and to rely on someone better qualified than them to decide what they should be wearing. And this is where it all starts to go wrong. If women are catered for by fashion or by designs that come from on high, then everything is all right. But if a woman's body or style is far removed from what fashion currently dictates then she will end up with hardly anything at all.

If ever the devil invented a way of working on women and how they view their bodies then fashion certainly was this way.

Women have been systematically drugged by the ease of ready-to-wear clothes and then, once dependent and submissive, they are told that their bodies are unsuitable for this clothing, which has been designed for those women the industry wants to flatter and protect. We will see in the next chapter, dealing with causes, the purpose behind this absurd practice, for there is indeed a reason for this lengthy conditioning and for creating such dependency.

For the time being, it is enough to know that fashion exists and, most importantly, it exists for particular shapes and sizes.

If you are one of the women who can fit inside this narrow tunnel, you will find something to wear, but others, all those with ample hips, proper womanly thighs and full breasts, will unfortunately be unable to wear the latest fashions. Up to a size 14, you can find what you need; anything larger and you have to make do with what is left. However, ask for a size 18 and this raises a smile; they hardly dare tell you but they have never heard the like. Still, they can suggest a few shops that stock outsizes.

I am not describing anything out of the ordinary as this scenario happens all the time. Open a women's magazine and you will see flashes of colour with an exotic backdrop and you too want the attractive outfit. You dash off to the shop stocking it, you try on the top which fits like a treat, then you ask for the skirt and, as you put it on in the hushed privacy of your changing room, you realize you cannot squeeze into it. And should you fail to notice yourself that it does not fit, you will soon have it pointed out to you. Your bottom or your hips do not fall within the norm. Whatever were you thinking of, having such rounded thighs! However desperately you tug away at the zip, the flesh won't give and the fastener won't close.

Once a woman has suffered this sort of misadventure too often, it puts her in a frame of mind that cuts her off from the group she so desperately wants to be part of and she will react in a far more serious and intense way than most men would imagine.

A woman's world and her femininity are very complex. A woman is tied to her family, her children and her husband, but she also belongs to the group in which she lives, even more so nowadays since women have launched themselves into professional careers and complex social relationships.

In consultations I regularly see women of this sort. Sometimes they are angry and rant and rave about the discrimination and choice some designer or other has imposed on them. Sometimes I see women, dumb-founded and resigned, ready to do whatever it takes to look like other women, like all those who to their mind are able to dress nicely.

Women feel ashamed of their bodies

If our women are subjected to a far more private anguish than the difficulty of finding something to wear it is because of the taboos against curves. However, the two torments are mutually supportive.

Surreptitiously and through lengthy brainwashing, as sly as it is patient, a gigantic noose has formed and tight-ened around women. It would be interesting to trace the history of this slippery slope and I will discuss it later on. What I have noticed is that, in 1935 – in other words, only three or four generations ago – there were still women who, in order to achieve an hourglass figure, would have their bottom two rib bones surgically removed.

And I did indeed say surgically, which meant opening them up with an incision on both sides of the back, and disarticulating both ribs where they joined the spine. This left behind two scars a few centimetres long. And do you know why these women wanted to undergo this operation? So that their newly sculpted waistline would emphasize their hips and thighs, producing a shape that men went crazy for at that time. Nowadays, surgeons are asked to suck the excessive curves out of women's thighs. How could we have gone from one extreme to another so quickly? It is not hard to work out, but discovering the precise reasons is more complex and I will explain why.

When designers ran out of new ideas for working with women's curviness, they went the other way and designed underwear that did not show off breasts or emphasize a full bottom, and then gradually they got rid of whatever else was holding the waistline in. Women could now breathe a little more easily but the men stopped panting. A definite shift had just taken place. There is always some fashion avant-gardist to push the boundaries a little further and a little harder than their predecessor and so gradually women's curves were whittled away.

The constant swing of fashion's pendulum has accustomed us to these fluctuations but usually it kept woman's natural, biological body firmly at the centre of any pirouettes. Then suddenly and for no apparent reason at all, having arrived at a new female archetype with healthy proportions, in fact one with few contrasts, something previously unheard of occurred. Designers pushed beyond what was possible for standard women and started designing for women who were not an average shape and had no hips, no thighs and no breasts.

It all started with Twiggy, arguably the most famous model the world has ever seen. I would not dare tell you how much money photographers offered her for an hour's sitting. A nineteenth-century woman would have despaired had she had a daughter with a body like hers and, had she lived at that time, Twiggy might have had great difficulty attracting a husband.

However, her portfolio proves that she definitely had no need for a marriage bureau. I do not believe that even Twiggy can have any idea of the number of photos taken of her. And these photos, do you know what happened to them? They were printed in black and white and in colour, in the American, French and Japanese press; in short, they appeared wherever a man or woman might be looking. And so Twiggy turned into a sort of mythological creature that could have devoured a quantity of paper equivalent to all the forests in Canada.

And all the while we were looking on and drinking up this magic potion which was throwing our urges and tastes into confusion. Earlier, I told you about a male lizard that was sexually disturbed by a female disguised as a male. This male lizard is not dissimilar to us poor men in the mid-1960s, presented with the new female icons who had bodies like beautiful Greek male adolescent statues. How were we then meant to react when we saw real breasts, proper thighs and bottoms? Once the newspaper was finished and we were lying next to a perfectly healthy woman, we then had to try to work out what we were meant to want. This was all very confusing for us men too.

Nonetheless, it was women who suffered most from this assault; it was women who slowly felt that they were becoming abnormal and different; and, as with a skin disease or allergy, shame about their own bodies started to make them feel uncomfortable all over. As soon as sex becomes involved, this shame begins to eat away; it becomes apparent first and foremost with partners, husbands and lovers.

How can you show a man your body when you are convinced that it is no longer the sort of body men are interested in? The answer is as simple as the question – you simply don't show it. Until the very last possible moment, you keep it camouflaged under protective veils. And then you quickly switch the lights off. I am not spinning a yarn but simply giving you an inkling of the confessions I hear all the time. You might well think that these women are hideous and deformed, and that to some extent their ploys are understandable. This is simply not the case. Most of the time, these women are absolutely normal. There is nothing at all repulsive about them and their husbands are at a complete loss to understand the reasons for the black out.

Of everything I have observed, this behaviour is perhaps the most odd and unexpected. Really obese women or even women with a very full figure have no such excessive modesty. Perhaps they have resigned themselves, or quite simply they think that what the eye cannot see, the hand can feel unequivocally.

The women that suffer the most are women with modest curves, and especially the prettiest ones. It is as if the more they try to achieve perfection, the less they are able to tolerate any imperfection; and the closer they get to their goal, the more impatient they become. Often the women who behave this way are the ones who cannot bear to be seen without make-up and rush off to make themselves beautiful as soon as they get out of bed in the morning.

Women who hate their curves are stricken by further, more serious confusion as misunderstandings arise when their partner caresses them, as happens whenever there is any attempt to have sex. A man's hand does not just roam haphazardly over a woman's body. His hand is seeking either to give pleasure or to receive some, and if possible to combine the two. A man is aroused by the rounded shape, touch and fullness of a woman's breasts, hips and thighs. Yet because culture has shunned them, these areas have become a source of shame and torment. So caressing them will always be very badly interpreted.

Sexual relationships are a means of communication when humankind returns to the sources of life; in other words, we retreat into our first instinctive brain and second emotional brain. The first brain communicates through sight, touch, smell and hearing. The second through emotional messages, facial expressions, noises, gestures, tears and groans.

The third, thinking brain has no business here. Its very presence inhibits us and we must do whatever we can to switch it off. Yet there is one situation where men can make use of this brain – namely, when they delay reaching orgasm by thinking of something other than the sex they are having. This shows us just how much damage the third brain can do when it is an unwelcome gate-crasher. Most cases of frigidity and impotence occur when the third brain gets involved in what is the business of the first two brains.

While we are on the subject, I have to tell you about the praying mantis, a particularly shocking example of animal sexuality. The female is an impressive size so when the mating season comes round the male cuts a sorry figure. Nevertheless, he does not resist the urge driving him to copulate. You all know the sad end awaiting him – without putting up a fight he is eaten alive during copulation. It is the sort of story that sticks in the mind, recounted with a wry smile within slightly feminist circles. No matter. What is far more interesting, and far less widely known, is that the male can only ejaculate once the female has devoured his head. If she did not do this there would be no fertilization. So now you can perhaps see the purely symbolic connection that I am trying to make with our own sexuality. The head gets in the way of the raw animality of the sexual act.

When we say that a woman is cerebral this means that she cannot prevent certain ideas from crossing her field of consciousness.

So the idea of a male hand finding its way into these shameful areas is exactly the kind of thought that inhibits. This means that if a woman does not accept her curves it can spell the beginning of sexual frustration. And if this happens too frequently, it will end up damaging her confidence about reaching orgasm, along with all the repercussions this is likely to have on her relationship.

Physiological consequences: slimming on purpose but to no purpose

We have looked at the psychological confusion women experience if they do not see themselves anywhere among our present-day archetypes, and the problems in dressing fashionably and expressing their sexuality which follow on from this. I conclude that for the past quarter of a century, biological femininity has been poles apart from cultural femininity.

I have given you the impression that, subjected to these constant attacks, the only thing left for women to do was to try to lose weight. Here I am entering familiar territory, where I have a privileged position as an observer. So I can talk about this from lengthy experience, but my focus is not on excessively plump or obese women as I have already written other books on the subject. Here I am interested only in women with a normal weight but who are obsessed with getting rid of their curves.

Who are these women and where do they come from?

Before examining in detail the various misconceptions and difficulties of slimming to no purpose, I would first of all like to talk to you about the women who seek out the help of a nutritionist. Who are they and where do they come from?

The question is perhaps a little blunt but the answer is very simple: the average woman on the street who comes from everywhere. What I mean by this is that there is absolutely nothing eccentric about these women; they have no particular psychological profile. The one thing they do have in common is a desire not to be excluded from the group to which they belong. I would go as far as to say that they often include women with quite distinct personalities, who can make firm decisions. Quite simply, they make their minds up quicker while other women spend their time thinking things over. You are perhaps curious to know what social strata they belong to. You might well think they come from the idle middle classes who have nothing else to worry about other than contemplating their own navels or bodies. Again, you would be quite wrong.

There are just as many working-class women as intellectuals, as many well-off middle-class women as young shop girls, and as many mothers with large families as young students. But what is most surprising of all is to find combatants from elite circles in among this battalion of frustrated women. And I mean women holding high levels of responsibility, women of action, authoritative managing directors, lawyers, erudite financiers, well-known journalists and even some doctors who feel somewhat ashamed to be reduced to this. Which speaks volumes about how strongly motivated they must be and tells us even more about the extent to which other women, with less lucidity and strength of character, submit to the cultural mantras that are alienating them without putting up any kind of fight.

What does fat do?

It is a good idea to answer this question so that we know what we can and cannot do to scale down our body's contours. Fat, or adipose tissue, is meant to be found under the skin and in between the organs it surrounds. It performs a triple role:

- It provides support; a little like straw placed around fragile objects in a packing case.
- It plays a role in storing energy. Nature had anticipated that we might have to alternate between times of famine and feast. When our food intake is rich and covers our daily energy requirements, any surplus is stored away as fat, its most concentrated form.
- Lastly, fat is a decorative and distinguishing feature.

This is where we first see fat being positioned for purely sexual reasons. Influenced by your hormones, and without you being warned or aware of it, some of your fat will find its way to areas that will develop a different shape depending on whether you are a man, a woman or a pre-pubescent child.

Before puberty, your body does not choose where this fat goes. A little girl will put on weight in the same way as her younger brother. However, as soon as her ovaries start working everything changes and fat finds its way into the areas that are unique to each gender. Under the careful guidance of femininity's hand, female fat rapidly gravitates to the breasts, hips and thighs.

Whenever a woman suddenly find she needs to draw upon these fat reserves, either because she has nothing left to eat – which nowadays is rare – or, which is far more frequent, because she has embarked on a diet, an internal metabolic process attacks the stored fat, turning it into sugar. I am sure you are aware of this, but what you may well not know is the order in which the fat melts away. The first to respond to the call is the fat on the face, torso and waist. If you keep going, the interstitial fat that supports your intestines will follow next; then watch out for your internal organs dropping. Decorative fat, the type we are interested in, which declares your gender and fills out your curves, will resist the call as it was not designed to obey your whims. It has far too important a role to play for nature to let you tamper with it for no good reason, and probably this fat is the cause of all your current consternation.

What is cellulite?

We are now treading on ground where words do not hold the same meaning for everyone and where, unfortunately, there are as many opinions as interested parties. Cellulite is a magic word that makes women tremble and men smile. It might be useful to clear things up a little.

I do not know who invented the word 'cellulite'. It is not correct but the collective mind has seized upon it so eagerly that it has taken on a life of its own and we are now stuck with it. The Anglo-Saxons have translated it using the term *cellulitis.*

For doctors, it is an inflammation of the connective tissue that intertwines through our adipose tissue. For women who read women's magazines, it is a shameful disease that spreads mainly on their hips and thighs.

How much truth is there in this? As I have told you, there is a fat whose job it is to give you feminine contours and it gives shape to your thighs, hips, knees and breasts. Without these features, you would not be put together in the normal way; however, variations from body to body reveal the different extent to which women are sensitive to the female hormone, folliculin.

If you are very feminine and react strongly to folliculin, then you will have a host of symptoms that offset certain advantages, and your contours, your mood and your behaviour will be very contrasting. If you do not respond to this hormone, you will be flat, without breasts or bottom; you will have some slight, strange down and a falsetto voice. However – and now we get to the pathological – if you have an unusually strong reaction to folliculin you are likely to see the appearance on your thighs of what people call cellulite.

This is an obvious and extensive infiltration of the gynoid areas. We are not talking now about body shape but about real distortion. This cellulite is hard and painful; it disrupts circulation by forming a tourniquet that stops the blood from flowing back – resulting in the infamous 'saddlebags' that deform and spread. Initially, it was a normal sign, then it went wrong. What is more, this symptom never comes on its own. Once cellulite becomes rife, you can be sure to find it in conjunction with what we call PMS – premenstrual syndrome – when a woman's hormones make her really suffer for ten days leading up to her period. She feels in a foul mood, she sleeps badly and not enough, she is constipated and feels bloated. She is thirsty but can no longer urinate and her clothes feel tight all over. Once her period starts, miraculously everything returns to normal within two or three days.

Should cellulite be treated? Definitely. Treating it is no picnic, though, since there is no question of reducing body mass without first of all regulating the underlying hormonal problems. And this is where the difficulty lies. Extreme care must be exercised when adjusting folliculin levels. Too brutal an intervention and periods can be disrupted and little signs of virilization are likely to appear, such as a light down over the skin or a change in voice. Unquestionably this must be left to the experts.

As for the parts of the body themselves, once they start to cause problems either because they are unsightly or because they are endangering adjacent areas, effective local treatments are available. But these are long and therefore require constant attention, a special diet and, above all, GP supervision throughout.

The only question that has to be answered, and answered unequivocally, is whether losing weight has any effect on cellulite. Well, the answer is no. You can lose as much weight as you want, but you stand no chance whatsoever of producing any effect on these diseased areas. And I will go even further. The more weight you lose, the more the fat distributed over the rest of your body will melt away. You will make your bust, waistline and face thinner; we will be able to count your ribs; your protruding shoulder blades will jut out – but the lower body you are furiously working away on will calmly resist all your efforts. And once your heroic attempts are over, what will you see? A body that is even more out of proportion than before and your cellulite, a pocket of ample flesh surrounded by skinniness, will become even more conspicuous, like a nose in the middle of a face.

The disasters of slimming to no purpose

In this chapter, and let's not forget this, I am talking about women who are perfectly healthy but cannot accept part of their authentic femininity. If I have dwelt upon certain weapons for tackling obesity, this is because unfortunately at times they end up being used and misused in instances where there is absolutely no need for them. Attempts to lose weight to no purpose end up being crowned by three serious consequences, each one of which is, in itself, far more serious than these unfortunate curves which men are perfectly comfortable with. You must bear these three disasters constantly in mind so as to avoid all temptation to reduce by force these wonderful symbols of gentleness.

Creating artificial obesity

You may be surprised to learn that by wanting to get rid of a little body mass you could end up becoming obese. Yet, more often than not, this is how it all starts. Imagine a gorgeous, healthy, feminine young woman with hips and thighs that are minding their own business and sending out their natural signals just as they should. The fortunate woman blessed with them is not so convinced of her good fortune and wants to look like our magazine heroines, so she gets it into her mind that she needs to lose weight.

Correctly supervised, and by using methods that target specific parts of her body, she may indeed lose – to my mind quite unnecessarily – some part of her unwanted femininity. In this case, there will be no further repercussions. However, if she takes it into her head that to achieve her target she wants to lose some weight, too, then everything becomes more complicated. Since she started out with a normal weight, she has got herself embroiled in losing weight for no purpose and wasting resources – and this the body does not like.

Kept in the dark, the poor thing has no idea where this is all heading. And at the very first opportunity when dieting gets forgotten, amid the elation of success, the body will work twice as hard and in a few weeks it will have put back on again what was lost with such great effort. However – and now is the time to really watch out – not content with taking back its due, and anxious about the deprivation it was subjected to, the body will exceed its target and add for good measure an extra four pounds to a weight that the young woman was already unhappy with. Disappointed, irritated, this woman, plagued by reactive bulimia, will eat more than ever, which will not solve anything. The end result will be almost an extra half-stone and all in the wrong place.

With the process now underway, we have quite unintentionally got caught up in experimental obesity. Six months go by and, with summer just round the corner, war is once more waged upon these curves that will have to be exposed on the beach. So around half a stone is lost and then once winter arrives, ten to twelve pounds pile back on. The end result is now an extra twelve pounds. And there is no reason at all why this pattern should stop.

I do not want to turn this book into a slimming guide, but if you are lucky enough to have a normal or slightly lower than normal weight, then leave it well alone, otherwise you are running a risk – the risk of losing a few pounds only to put far more back on and get embroiled in a vicious circle which can only end in obesity.

After the age of thirty, losing weight makes you age

Once again, I am aiming my remarks at women who have a normal weight, but who are tempted to lose a few pounds to get rid of the shapely contours that have gone out of fashion. Apart from the futility, they run a particular risk if they are over the age of thirty. Because however furiously they diet, the volume of their thighs will not concede even half an inch, whereas the face responds straightaway; the slightest deprivation and it becomes gaunt. So then you find yourself caught in the odd dilemma of having to choose between the lower and the upper body, between body mass that is hidden away or a face that is on permanent display.

Presented with this choice, who wouldn't choose the face? Unfortunately, women always opt for their thighs while the face is left to fade away. From my work as a nutritionist, I have discovered a law about female beauty.

In absolute terms, and to age as little as possible, the ideal scenario would be to remain slim until the age of thirty and put on a little weight every year until the menopause. Just a few ounces a year are all it takes to temper the unappealing effects of age. As the skin starts to sag with time, it is a good idea to stretch it slightly from the inside to make up for any loss of elasticity. But would any woman nowadays go along with this sort of precept? Blindness is in our minds, and one day we will end up sitting on our faces to show off an android bottom.

Before the age of thirty, losing weight can cause periods to stop

This is very commonly observed and we do not really know quite how or why, but whenever a young girl's body is put under too much strain, by making it lose weight beyond what is biologically acceptable, her periods become very irregular or stop altogether. Young girls or women who have not yet had children should take particular note of this. Everything leads us to believe that a young body responds very badly to any extensive incursions into thinness territory. And perhaps this is the body's way of letting us know that it has been given a rough time; a trauma or emotional upset produces the same effect. It is very important that this amputation of a woman's femininity is not treated lightly, as I have known personally women whose periods have never come back, meaning that they would never be able to enjoy motherhood. Once again, care needs to be exercised, so that something superfluous does not jeopardize a woman's chances of having a baby.

The pill and curves

It would have been difficult for me to end this chapter without discussing the pill. Although dear to men's hearts, women's curves are out of favour with women. This anachronism is the central theme of my book. However, I am aware – and I am talking to you now as a doctor – that the pill is a form of contraception that can lead to weight gain. But not the sort of weight that may leave you unconcerned; instead it is the weight that turns into body mass and plagues your thighs.

I am delighted to present you with this dilemma, where you are faced with a conflicting choice in which two cultural imperatives come into direct opposition.

You have to choose between, on the one hand, responding to the legitimate need to choose when your lovemaking might result in procreation and, on the other hand, following blindly and against all reason the canons for this current fashion for emaciation. And I admit that here you do spend a long time before making up your minds. However, mostly you won't take my word for it, so you feel like trying the experiment. And I for one am certainly not going to stop you, since you know my thoughts on women's curves. Unfortunately, the test is always conclusive and your thighs will not resist. Once again you are confronted with your initial choice. This is the time I choose to reiterate my message to you. Everything would fit into place if you could free yourself, even in part, from this taboo on curves. Your femininity is begging for it and men would not believe their eyes. Who would lose out? Nobody would. Fashion designers and ready-to-wear clothing manufacturers would be forced to go along with you because, after all, you keep them in work. However, I realize that my voice alone will not sway you so in part three I will appeal to all those people who are better placed than me to work on your subconscious.

Confusion in men

This book is not just directed at women. With time I have come to realize that all the logical arguments that can be mustered carry little weight when they come up against the omnipotence of our collective subconscious. Nonetheless, I hope to play some part in getting the ball rolling. But getting what ball rolling exactly? I know who is responsible for the frustration you women currently feel. However, the ogre who is feeding away on your misery is far too wily to act openly. It prefers to dispatch its orders to your subconscious structures and to your innate desire to belong to the group. In this way, it outsmarts any attempt to act consciously. So the only appropriate way to respond will be to send out signals using its own wavelengths and we will discover how to do this later on.

In the meantime, I need men's help because although these cultural dictates and mantras are also directed at them, men are not so much the target. And they still retain some independence which rational arguments may work on.

These taboos on women's curves concern men too, because a man is connected to his partner by emotional and sexual bonds that are strengthened through each other. However, his status as a man living in a complex society means that he chooses for himself a spouse who has to fulfil two requirements.

. The first is that she pleases him personally and the harmony I have in mind here is more akin to nature than culture. You will no doubt protest, but I have to say it: the individual, fundamental harmony between a man and a woman has to develop through their sexual relationship. The equation for this harmony encompasses an array of signs that may appear trivial but, as far as biologists and ethologists are concerned, they are becoming ever more relevant all the time.

You certainly pay no attention to smell, and the touch of the skin may seem of minor importance to you; without you being in any way conscious of it you are charmed by the shape of hips and the roundness of breasts and certain attitudes. You look into your partner's eyes and her pupils dilate particularly widely. When you touch her, she shows rapid signs of sexual interest and finally the orgasm you give her and her tender, satisfied behaviour as she unconsciously expresses her gratitude are all messages that bundle together and reach your first and second primitive brains, where they work away without you even being aware of it. In the meantime, your third brain, the one that is hired to rationalize and provide alibis for all your decisions, is telling you that this woman is cultured, beautiful, intelligent, shares the same beliefs as you, that she dresses well, is sophisticated and well educated, good company and, in all good faith, you think that if you have chosen her then it is down to all these reasons. In fact, they do not count in your decision, but they do count for the group within which you live. The basic cement binding you together is the one hidden from you, the one you try to describe with words such as 'charm', 'magical' moments and 'ambiance' and that certain 'je ne sais quoi' as you attempt to explain what we cannot explain to ourselves.

And what is most amazing about the revelations behavioural science is currently uncovering is that these messages are very selective. Body odours and dilating pupils, for example, which play such an enormous and unseen role when two people first meet, are highly personalized. There are no two women in the world with exactly the same odour and even if you do not know this, you can smell it. And her pupils are dilating for you only; the dilation is not directed at the man standing next to you, and you feel its impact without even noticing it.

Nevertheless, on your way home, you will say to yourself, 'What enjoyable conversation, what beautiful hair.' Yet she might just as well have worn a hat or not uttered a single word; it would not have made the slightest difference. Biological communication would still have been established. And I am not even talking about body, hands or voice. We have not yet discovered all there is to find out, as biology will have more to tell us tomorrow about man's basic motivations. What surprises we have in store! I remain convinced that one day we will understand precisely what is meant by so common and prosaic a statement as 'to have someone under your skin'.

The second reason for the choice you make has to do with your cultural context. A lot of very social men would rather sacrifice their biological aspirations and marry a woman from a similar background, a 'suitable' woman. Yet we know that this sort of appropriate marriage is likely to fizzle out quickly if it is not kept alight by the magic of primitive communication. Nonetheless, we should not underestimate these social reasons.

As far as women's curves are concerned, men are faced with a strange choice nowadays. These curves play a very important role in a man's sexual relations and his primitive communication. Depending on how clear-headed he is, he may or may not be aware of this. But, on the other hand, the society in which he lives wants nothing to do with these curves and devalues them. A man's wife is his partner, his other half, but she is also an outward sign of power and wealth. Men with beautiful wives have always been envied and therefore held in high esteem. So it is important for him that she is beautiful not only in his eyes but in other people's eyes too. Whenever he goes out, it matters to him that she is the best dressed woman, and even if he does not especially like her wearing make-up, he will turn a blind eye to it when guests have been invited. Jewellery, perfume, beauty treatments and elegance – often this is all for going out and once the evening is over what do earrings or diamond rings matter to him?

It is just the same for her curves. In the depths of his old, male subconscious, he enjoys them, and without him really realizing it, they help him love his partner. However, when in society, he would prefer to be able to do without them. You don't need to be a mathematician to work out that to satisfy both demands he would need two women: one to go out with and one to come home with. All I am doing here is explaining old clichés.

And when a wife, who has beautiful, harmonious womanly curves, like a bride who is too beautiful, makes up her mind to get rid of them and tells her husband about it, conflict arises inside this man between what is conscious and subconscious in his own brain. He does not say yes but he does not say no either and, unable to bear the awkward contradiction, he just lets things take their course. This is where we have got to at present. Men are wavering between social appearances and what their hands and eyes demand.

Unfortunately, hands and eyes do not speak out and will never proclaim how much it may cost them to lose some part of their *raison d'être*.

If you are at all unsure of this, then compare what husbands and wives read and you will understand. Women delight in looking at glossy fashion photos in their women's magazines. You know much better than I do that the models you find here are clothes hangers with all-purpose, beautiful faces and bodies without any rough edges which allow the clothes to hang correctly. You do not even see it, you can sense it; the insidious message gets across and worms its way into the female subconscious.

As for men, take a closer look at how they loiter in newsagents. They wander around, flick through a few magazines and in passing just happen to open a *Playboy* or some other men's magazine. If they are brave enough, and some men are, they will buy it.

Take a look too at the sort of film actresses men like. And to push our survey as far as curiosity can go, try to find out who forms the juries that vote for Miss World or Miss Europe. Men, always men, and now you understand why the beauty queens in question invariably have breathtaking personal statistics. The American actor and film director, Raoul Walsh, said: 'Take any woman with a faded face and put her in a tight-fitting T-shirt without a bra, and all eyes will be drawn to her.'

A couple where the woman is regularly losing weight and desperately trying to look like the emaciated models she sees everywhere around her all the time is a couple in danger. Because sexual relations, which have a natural tendency to run out of steam, are going to fizzle out far quicker in these artificial circumstances. If women continue to try to look like their size-zero icons, if they lose their freshness, their curves and their smells, then they will end up losing their husbands too. For there are still some rare beauties, who are sufficiently straightforward and intuitive to understand, despite all the brainwashing, that their most precious asset is precisely what all other women are rejecting. So be on your guard if a woman like this shows any interest in your man!

Therefore, men, I need you, when the moment is right, to add your immense weight to the argument. Up until now men have not got involved. They have no wish to get mixed up in these women's matters; they may well on occasion have a good old moan but they dread appearing old-fashioned. One more chapter and it will be time to act. So, men, get yourselves prepared because if the plan works then, as they say in English, you will be able to 'have your cake and eat it'. You will be able to have just one woman, a woman you are happy to go out with and take to bed too.

7. What has led to the taboo on women's curves?

You may well think that the fascination with thinness is due to some passing, trivial fad and is of little consequence, and that when all is said and done there is not that much to worry about. First of all, this would mean closing our eyes to the suffering endured by women who cannot identify with our current archetypes. These frustrations remain hidden from men but are very real indeed.

However, what is far more important is to see that for the first time ever we are rejecting a natural, biological feature that was created for specific purposes around two to three million years ago. We are so brainwashed that we no longer pay much attention to women's curves. They have become trivialized, and most of you perhaps still doubt whether they can have the same impact as a bosom, a feminine voice or having no body hair. Yet they are a physical feature and as far as our evolution and our success as a species are concerned, women's curves are just as important as any body organ. So they are part of our inheritance, and the fact that they are currently banished feels to me like a loss or amputation.

What does worry me is that in the rest of the living world, whenever an animal refuses to behave naturally or amputates some part of itself this happens because the group in which it is living is threatened with extinction. As banal as this symptom may appear to you, we must look upon our contempt for the female body shape as one of the ways in which our Western civilization is going wrong.

The soaring growth in the population as we run out of resources, pollution, the increase in criminality and crime, loss of respect for the family and the extreme appeal of drugs – all these are other dangers that will seem to you more serious and threatening.

Personally, I am more fearful about the loss written over women's bodies, as to me it seems to herald something far more alarming – namely, the obliteration of the difference between the sexes and, in the long term, the risk this poses for the family which is already in poor health. And the family is the base of every society, every culture and every civilization.

Throughout history, once a civilization fell like a ripened fruit because it had run its natural course, there were other more vigorous, and often more primitive, peoples to take over and create a new civilization. Nowadays, our civilization has spread right across the world and, if we fall, we will be the last ones.

It is always a little destabilizing when a tradition, a fashion or cultural rite is lost, but to reject a part of the body that is stuck in our flesh, which conveys messages of gender difference, creates desire and pleasure and encourages reproduction, is a serious matter and this rejection heralds stormy times ahead.

If our society has encouraged the sacrifice of such an invaluable characteristic this is because behind apparently perfectly harmless appearances, very powerful, hidden reasons are bound to have played a decisive role. This is my opinion. This chapter on the causes for the taboo on women's curves will answer three obvious questions: Who is issuing the dictates? Who is passing them on? And why do our women go along with them?

Who is issuing the dictates? Our consumer society and feminism

At the bottom of everything, there is as always a biological bedrock. An old instinct, combined with a new brain, paved the way that led humankind inevitably to our highly technological and globalized culture. How was it that two biological characteristics, already there in Cro-Magnon man, were able to make us achieve such feats? Let us take a look at these two primitive, human attributes.

Man creates tools: homo faber

Our instinct for exploring
This is not an instinct that is peculiar only to humankind; it is found in all animals. If you place a mouse in a room with which it is unfamiliar, or in a labyrinth, and if at the same time you offer it some food, it will only take an interest in the food once it has completely explored its

new territory – and it will do this even if it is starving. In biological terms, we say that its exploratory behaviour was stronger than its feeding instinct. We may conclude, in our naïvety, that such an animal is curious. However, what we do not realize is that this curiosity is firmly hard-wired into its brain structures.

This instinct fulfils a very specific purpose, which is to allow the animal to discover other food supplies and find out about any nearby dangers. It means the animal is far more likely to survive. Eating without knowing whether their territory is safe would mean taking a risk that rodents will always avoid.

Man is one animal whose exploratory behaviour is pushed to its most extreme limits. From childhood onwards, humans show a total interest in anything new, which forces anxious parents to supervise their children very closely so that dangerous experiences are avoided. No nook or cranny, no object escapes their attention, but hardly has the child's curiosity been satisfied and off it goes again on an insatiable quest to explore everything, and this impulse lasts into adulthood. You might think that it would all stop here, which does sometimes happen. However, the baton is now passed on to professional explorers, the men and women who have mapped out every corner of the world, descended into the oceans' depths and scaled inaccessible mountain tops. Even the moon has felt the effects of our old exploratory instinct. Yet at the same time – and this is what holds the greatest interest for us – we have also carried out this exploration on ourselves. A scientific researcher is an explorer, delving into the laws of nature, and intellectual curiosity has shown that this exploration has no bounds.

A mutation: the new human brain

Our new human brain is eighty thousand years old and has fourteen billion cells. It is the result of the great mutation that enabled us to think and most importantly to survive. What would have become of us, poor, isolated primates, without the strength of the gorilla and the baboon's sharp canine teeth? Defenceless and unable to hunt, our wonderful brand-new brain would have finished up in the clutches of a predator.

Yet, as if by a miracle, this astounding organ gradually started to work and it allowed us to create and to invent. Our curiosity stirred its potential into action and a simple pebble in man's hand turned into our first weapon and our first tool. Nature had given us an organ thanks to which we would over time make the most of an immense range of possibilities. The weapon or tool proved to be an extension of our hand and we annexed them without the least hesitation. Combined, these two components of human nature were going to take us a long way, as we shall now see.

The inevitable march of progress

You must be thinking that we have left the taboo on women's curves far behind and this is true. In such distant times, as I have already told you, the most beautiful women were selected because of their curves. This new brain had not yet got involved with feminism. But have patience, we will get there.

For the time being, we have got as far as the axe and then the bow and arrow. And as soon as one new invention appears, instead of it being patented and kept secret, it is immediately passed on and shared, becoming part and parcel of humankind's capital. Fire was rapidly mastered, which meant metals could be worked and weapons became increasingly sophisticated. The wheel, which seems so obvious to us, represented a huge step forwards. However, we are not here to chart the initial stages in humankind's inventiveness. We need only note that a shift had taken place which enabled our sense of exploration to delve around in nature and take control of it. Next agriculture and cattle rearing freed us once and for all from having to hunt and the permanent obligations that hunting entailed.

From now on, man's hands were free to build the first great civilizations. And the inventions kept coming thick and fast, bringing in their wake the benefits of technology. The comfort and well-being they provided must have been interpreted as rewards.

Since then, we have not stopped moving forwards, understanding and discovering, and the prestigious name of 'progress' has been attributed to this activity. At the outset, this term had a very prosaic meaning as all it signified was to go forwards. However, noting that taking this

direction brought with it Father Christmas-like bountiful-
ness, we started investing it with mythological
significance.

From then on, and in particular since the industrial
age, there has been a veritable war of religions as the
champions of progress oppose any reactionaries who
attempt to rein in this runaway horse. Yet to no avail. We
will have to wait until our instinctive curiosity starts
interfering with the nuclei of atoms and, even more sacro-
sanct, with human cells before far-sighted consciences
start to ask themselves searching questions about the
true value of progress. However, the nuclear bombs are
already in their silos and impatiently await our final
answer.

The consumer society

Everything was fine until machines appeared. With
energy tamed and controlled, industrial machinery was
able to replace human workmanship. The last of the trade
and craft guilds died out as the temptation to produce
overshadowed any nostalgia.

Ever since then, the machines have been working at
full capacity, with production becoming the main index
of wealth for a civilized nation.

However, and here we come back to our theme, there
would be no point at all in producing if there was not a
huge mass of consumers, all herded together. So, great
efforts were made to satisfy their every whim. The slightest thing they longed for was translated into punch cards,

and straightaway the objects of their desire left our assembly lines in their thousands.

However, very quickly two obstacles emerged that mirror the paradox of our civilization. As it was systematically satisfied, this desire for goods finally dried up because consumers, overwhelmed with products, became few and far between. Yet the machines kept on working, and, like a famished Minotaur, demanded a new cartload of victims day after day.

The first difficulty could be circumvented by conditioning our motivations differently. You no longer have any desires; alright then, we will take it upon ourselves to find you some. And this is where the new culture got involved. Helped by advertising and the media, it skilfully contrived to create new needs for us. This was the time of the automobile industry, the telephone, the washing machine, and then things we had no need for as advertising brainwashed us into becoming dependent on electronic gadgets and the rather childish joy of pushing buttons.

The second difficulty was a little harder to get round. When consumers became thin on the ground, they had to be seduced and tracked down to wherever they might still be hiding. But once the last few reluctant ones had been flushed out from their hideaways, only one solution remained, and we turned our attention to our underdeveloped neighbours. This was the period of economic imperialism and colonialism and we all know where it ended. Faced once again with no takers, only women were left. Feminism came striding on to the scene and, in its wake, the taboo on women's curves.

Psychoanalyzing a civilization: feminism

If we take time to consider the great civilizations that have come before us, we cannot fail to notice that the life and energy pulsing through them were due to scientific discoveries and the technological progress that these generated. But alongside the technological innovations, culture, tastes, arts and fashions changed too, altering ways of life.

Nowadays, at the heart of our industrial society, a culture has emerged that has given us a taste for unbridled consumption. The 'American way of life' has long since swept across our planet and were it to explode one day, a future explorer from Mars would very likely puzzle long and hard over the Coca-Cola bottles to be found among all our ruins.

However, let us concentrate on how this culture, by serving economic imperatives, gave rise to feminism.

Up until the Second World War, each purchasing power was represented by one family and one pay packet, that of the husband. Once this purchasing power had reached its limits and economic disaster loomed, the idea surfaced from across the Atlantic that an attempt could be made to encourage women to become consumers in their own right. This promised to double the potential for absorbing the market's products.

But for this to happen, women had to be autonomous and, most importantly, they had to work. In Latin countries, where traditions are not tampered with, interfering in such a way with the woman's role as housewife and her husband's role as protector made this a rather difficult undertaking. However, the economy does not overburden itself with such scruples.

Its means are determined by its goals. It wanted women, and it would have them, whatever the price family and society would have to pay. One after the other, every attempt at resistance was undermined, not openly but totally subconsciously through a haze of sound rational and moral reasons. And women were not brought down by force, but rather through cunning and by being 'drugged'.

Firstly, the consumption drug was injected and conditioning was patiently hardwired into our neural pathways. Just like Pavlov's dogs, we started salivating at the thought of any sort of household gadget or new item of clothing. We were made to dream of frozen food then freezers, then video players, exotic holidays and canned sunshine. All on credit and delivered to our homes.

Once the drug was well enough in place, and addiction had made us dependent, the men felt unable to cope alone. They could no longer cater for all these needs on their own. So either we had to go back to how things had been and partly wean ourselves off the addiction or else move forward determinedly and embrace the working woman's new status. Nowadays, half of all women who live in and around Paris go out to work.

The consumption drug was violent and even brutal, but on its own it was not enough to unbolt the biological structures that go back to the first generations of men, which determine how work is allocated. So our new culture's sirens' song was enlisted, using good humanitarian and moralizing reasons to transfix and, most importantly, the double-message brainwashing technique.

A society can be psychoanalyzed, just like an individual. You simply have to get it to lie down on a couch and let it speak. If you point out that, for the past two million years, all previous civilizations have invariably accepted man's law, a legacy from the animal world, and that despite a few misuses things were not that bad, why then has there been this recent trend for militant feminism? It will reply:

- *Times have changed; women have become clear-sighted and have at last opened their eyes to how men kept them enslaved.*
- But why has this only happened since the end of the Second World War? There was nothing to stop them being clear-sighted in the eighteenth or nineteenth centuries. George Sand, the nineteenth-century French novelist, certainly thought about it, so why didn't all other women? Slaves have been rebelling since Spartacus, and surely the right moment would have been during the French Revolution?
- *No, the time had not come; science had not made*

sufficient progress and the opposition's political forces were not in place.

- But why are men happy now to allow this autonomy and sexual freedom of which they used to be so jealous and so possessive?
- *Because they have finally woken up to the fact that they were in the wrong and they had to give way because there are many women out there set on change.*

The conversation could go on and on, but it would only reveal the alibi narrative, the conscious narrative. Whereas the subconscious narrative, the one that has to be kept hidden away because it is shameful, says that this is happening because the production ogre needs to be fed and liberated women will do this very nicely, thank you.

From then on, the feminism that people wanted and economic circumstances had made possible would forge its battle ideology and promote its own cultural norms, which would include a new concept of the body and would specifically reject women's curves.

And it is here, at the heart of a movement that is spreading across the globe, that we find the same double message:

The subconscious language, which is controlling operations behind the scenes, rejects all idea of sexual poles. Men and women are equals, so anything that highlights their differences is bad for the doctrine. Wherever there is any divergence between the sexes in behaviour, taste or fashion, these gaps had to be closed, so that the same salaries, the same rights and the same sexual and economic freedom could be laid down.

As for our bodies, even if it seemed unthinkable, any differences that were too visible had to be toned down and anything that reeked of sexual polarity and was not vital had to be eliminated.

This is the language that is fed to women so that they can trot out arguments, this alibi language that thinks it is conscious. And as always, it is a humanitarian and moralistic narrative that talks about the 'beautiful', the 'good' and 'well-being'.

All of a sudden, what had always been thought of as unacceptable for women became 'beautiful'. Small, android breasts stuck on top of sticky–out ribs became the 'in' thing; bras were now old-fashioned, unnecessary, as voluptuous breasts were deemed vulgar and now there was no holding back on referring to them in derogatory terms. As for hips and thighs, they became unwieldy, worrying body mass that was upsetting the body's harmony. It would take a heroic effort to remain lucid and withstand this tsunami of messages.

As if this language about what is 'beautiful' were not enough, the chorus next chimed in with what is 'good', based on pseudo-medical twaddle. The craftiest piece of nonsense was the invention of cellulite, a word that can make even the most intelligent women shudder. A little roundness and the slightest curve and your thighs would now be dubbed saddlebag or jodhpur thighs. You are told with absolute conviction that this will obstruct circulation, and you need to lose weight quickly to avoid getting varicose veins and stretch marks. And should you be impudent enough to cast doubt on this, you will be told that your weight is excessive, you face a whole array of health risks, you are riddled with cholesterol and any minute now you will turn all flabby.

Finally, the idea of your 'well-being' is kept for last, as no objections can remain to counter this argument. Now we have reached the realm of collective hysteria. And quite clinically, without the slightest fear of appearing ridiculous, like a leitmotif, you are told over and over again that carrying an extra four or five pounds is not 'good' for your 'well-being'.

The slightest effort and you get out of breath, you feel heavy, congested, and you are no longer as alert and lively. How ever did our poor mothers manage back then, carrying an extra 10–15 per cent body weight, while still being considered slim for the period?

The aim is to reduce the differences between the sexes

Most important for the feminists was first of all to win women over to their way of thinking. Believe me, this has not been easy; and their ideology still meets with great resistance because, contrary to everything people try to make us believe, women instinctively sense what I would call their role and function.

The feminists' project took on a mystical aura because of the word 'equality': a word that encompasses a noble aspiration nobody could rightly take issue with. However, protected by this unassailable battle flag, we have slowly drifted away from an ideal of the sexes being equal to the horrendous notion of the sexes being identical.

Swept away with enthusiasm for their just cause, to obtain the same rights as men, feminists unconsciously got involved in a futile attempt to abolish differences.

Anything different turned into something unequal and this rapidly drifted towards the idea of inferiority. With this idea, feminism had found its niche, its best arguments and the best way of winning over hearts and minds. And it was in this climate of merging and mixing that war was declared upon differences.

But a woman *is* fundamentally different from a man. To convince herself of this, she need only listen to her voice and look at herself in a mirror and see her face, waistline, bosom, hips and skin.

As regards behaviour, emotions and sexuality, people dared say there was a strict identity and that subservience through the ages had created and engineered a purely cultural archetype. I do not know who it was that said a woman was not born a woman but became one. Or rather, I know all too well. So then, before you become a woman, what can you be exactly? An asexual, undifferentiated being or a man perhaps?

I would not dare exploit arguments connected with women's menstrual cycles or motherhood, as that would be just too easy. Her sexual life is itself so distinct from and so complementary to man's sexual life! This is so well known and beyond the scope of my topic.

However, just as a matter of interest, I will tell you that a statistically large enough proportion of women, full of folliculin a few days before their period, feel 'compelled to clean and tidy', i.e. at a time when they are awash with hormones and so at their most feminine.

Who would believe me? Yet it is true, and I know that as they read these lines, some women will identify with this uncontrollable urge to rearrange the furniture and get everything shipshape.

What matter: men and women's behaviour patterns and emotions are so wonderfully different that it would take another book to compare both psycho-affective profiles. What I am concerned with is the female body, and as physique is where there are such great contrasts, it is here that the mantras have been the most offensive and the dictates the most blinding. Since the physical differences between men and women are so striking, they risked upsetting the feminists' whole theory, so they went for the impossible and the impossible was achieved. For this to happen, all it took was a continual battering away of messages promulgating new fashions and attacking anything that might distinguish women from men, so as to lessen the differences.

Let us try to briefly list them:

Hair

Traditionally women have long hair and men short hair.

Systematically, fashions were selected that overturned this natural tendency. All it took was the Beatles' mythical aura and the long locks of the French pop star Antoine, and healthy, rebellious young men let their hair grow long. This was the beatnik and hippy style which has been replaced today with ponytails, earrings and body piercing.

As for women, in France it all started with the actress Jean Seberg, whose short, cropped hair encapsulated a look and made every style variation possible.

Since then women's hairstyles have varied in length, but have never gone back to being nun-like.

Body hair

We still have not managed to find a way of making women hairy. So men's beards and moustaches had to be made unfashionable.

Nowadays, sporting a moustache is deemed vulgar, and beards are for old fogeys. All current adverts favour 'closely shaven' men.

Trousers

For a long time trousers were only worn by men, but this is no longer the case and so much so that the expression 'wearing the trousers' to denote a bossy and virile woman has become virtually obsolete.

The first women who dared to wear trousers were some rather absurd, fine ladies beautiful and eccentric enough to get away with it. And then any number of eccentrics came along and be-trousered women were no longer shocking. The eye gets used to everything, and although this story is only symbolic, it does tell us an awful lot.

The first trousers did at least take women's body mass into account, allowing their hips and thighs to breathe while cinching in at the waist and calves. Then jeans appeared and with them the first universal piece of unisex clothing. The word had been uttered and this single term sums up the whole doctrine and the whole horror of losing bipolarity.

Nowadays, if you see a man's sweater you like, you can ask if it is available for women too and you will be told it is a unisex item. Shirts, polo shirts, socks are all unisex. If women want a tie, they only have to choose. They will even sell you genuine 'GI' American army surplus trousers with a proper military belt that you will have to pull in really tight if you don't want to end up with them round your ankles.

And how did a woman manage to squeeze her body inside a pair of unisex jeans? This beggars belief. The male sales assistant would coolly suggest she lie down in order to pull up the zip. It was the only possible way to squeeze a pelvis into jeans that were never intended for this shape.

You may well have heard how women protested when Coco Chanel dared present her first suit. It was only the equivalent of the type of suit men were wearing and at the time it still came with a skirt. Today this suit is the prototype of the most traditional outfit there is for women. Try asking a young woman why she enjoys wearing trousers. She will never give you the only obvious, logical and genuine reason, which is to copy men. She will follow the mantras and trot out the standard reply: because trousers look good and above all they are practical. But if they really did look that good, then why wait until after the Second World War? And what is so practical about them? They take twice as long to get on.

All truths are not so easy to tell.

Shoulders

Everything would be so simple if men's wonderful shoulders, which give them such an imposing presence, could be erased in a trice with a miracle rubber. As yet, no such rubber exists, but we can do better – we can make them unfashionable.

What has happened to our wonderful strongmen, to those shoulders of yore? What could be more old-fashioned than a bodybuilder? Even beach lifeguards no longer dare to strut around. They have all been banished to fairs, circuses and non-chic beaches.

As fashion holds sway, men's epaulettes have disappeared. Women's designers have grabbed them instead. Do you remember Thierry Mugler's collections with his astronaut outfits for women? All that was missing were the helmets and serial numbers!

Shoes

The human race has never liked its feet. Yet as we stood up, leaving our ape origins behind us, it was our feet that bore the weight.

High heels make women's legs look more slender and at the same time they accentuate the curve of her back and emphasize her buttocks. This was too risky. So heels were scaled down and women were even encouraged to do away with them altogether and wear flat-heeled boots. I know young secretaries who think nothing of spending a third of what they earn in a month on a pair of these boots, and if this is beyond their means, heel-less unisex moccasins will do instead.

On the other hand, the fashion for men is raised heels – three, then four, then five extra centimetres. And if we did not have such hairy calves, we would be in Capri pants by now.

Women's curves

But the most radical mutation in ideas and tastes, the most vehement and most unrelenting change possible took place on this most sacred territory.

A woman's curves are a whole and on their own symbolize her femininity and what is most sexual about her. They are a symbol, but also a trigger signal, an ignition key for everything that can arouse a man's libido. How often do I have to repeat it? Men love women with curves; they don't love fat women or overweight women but they do love women with these wonderful curves that they can see and touch, and that are resilient enough to resist the pressure of their fingers and the intensity of their stares.

The violence of the reaction against these curves provides me with all the proof I need. Feminist ideologies and society, desperate to erase all differences, summoned to battle their best troops, their biggest advertising budgets and their fiercest and longest-running brainwashing campaign.

If these curves had been of so little importance, far less effort would have been expended and the message would not have been hammered out so insistently. If things went so far and at such a pace, then this was because women's curves were the last bastion. They had to be dismissed from favour, rendered shameful, unfashionable and lopped off. Or else the battle was lost.

And the battle has been so well fought that today you have to be a brazen hussy, a 'lost woman', to dare wear tight-fitting or revealing clothes.

Cellulite was invented for everyone; these vile 'saddlebags' for the slightest hint of a curve. Even men, programmed through and through to react to the first sign of a curve, are hesitant and uncertain. They no longer know what to make of such a contradictory message. Instinct drives them forward, and culture drives them back.

You cast a furtive glance at a woman's behind, and she turns sideways to remove its shape and meaning from view. You want to take a closer look and the lights get turned off. You put your hand there and she goes into a frenzy. The compass no longer points north but south. We are in great danger of losing our way once and for all.

However, one lost battle does not determine the outcome of the war. Culture is what a society or even a civilization produces. No matter how solid the underlying ideology may be, it is only ever the product of the 'human computer' and because of this it can and must get worn out.

What does last, what bends but does not break, is human nature. I know because I love reading history that no culture can resist our programming for long and that we revert to type. We wanted to experiment with removing the differences between the sexes and in part we succeeded, but as long as there is still one mother left on earth to raise her daughter to be a real woman, there is no reason for me to utterly despair.

In part three, I will make my modest contribution to reinstate the values that underlie femininity. The cultural dictates have already started to become less strident.

Sexual freedom
Before leaving behind the ideology that is very largely responsible for the taboo on women's curves, I would like to quickly examine how our sexual relations stand, to see if they have managed to resist our consumer society.

The differences that once so clearly distinguished the sexes have been reduced and there is no doubt that men are now less virile and women less feminine. The signals that both poles send out have become weaker. What are the repercussions of all this and how has our sexuality reacted to such distortions?

Have you ever observed a modern dance floor? People no longer dance cheek to cheek but in groups. You dance as part of a shapeless mass where everyone moves to a common beat. The only time you can feel and touch each other and pass on any pre-sexual message is when a slow dance is played.

Nowadays, in fashionable clubs, slow numbers are not played any more so you wait in vain for these few minutes of truth. What has happened to those body-to-body tangos and polkas, when your hands had to remain clamped to your partner's hips? Such dances are no longer in fashion and a single bar of these two dances would bankrupt the most independent of nightclubs. Isn't this a sure sign of the way we have distanced ourselves sexually?

Yet at the same time total sexual freedom is promoted, as the general public clamours for more. Pornography has its fans, while there are none for censorship. What have we done with all this freedom? I think we do make use of it but I am not sure whether this is always to any useful purpose.

I have already talked about the role sex plays in establishing the permanent bond between a man and a woman. For this bond to develop there has to be sexual attraction. Nature had programmed the game rules, with signals to get it started, transmitters and receivers. You know what happened to them. The bond gets off to a bad start. The first moment of magic underpinned by these biological messages has lost its effect. Moreover, each partner is aware that there are many more members of the opposite sex out there.

An eye not properly fixed on a single partner continues to rove over other available and sexually liberated rivals.

If desire is left to simmer away for too long, it runs the risk of evaporating. You end up compromising on the exposure time so the photo comes out blurred. The cement does not set and the bond gives way. This explains why it is difficult nowadays for couples starting out to give their relationship that special and sacred quality on which it should be based.

I do not want to get into a sociological study of couples. But this sacred element stems from the gap between what our instincts say and what our reason tells us. When our instincts speak out and our reason fails to understand them, we talk about magic, mythology and the irrational, and this all leads to the sacred. And from the sexual bond to love there is just one step that we are not good at explaining to ourselves.

From a deep and meaningful look to the emotion this triggers inside us, from the signals that emanate from a body to the energy that drives us to possess it, there are only natural forces at work here. To try to deny this is to be afraid of words, which does not prevent our deepest nature from carrying on regardless and continuing to do her best for us in spite of ourselves.

That our reason does not understand our instincts may be common, but all the same whenever a man runs his eyes or hands over a woman's body nature continues to

211

do her work. Perhaps with a little more difficulty, as there is hesitation and resistance, but I do believe and hope that nature is still effective enough for there still to be love.

A woman who really cares about being recognized as a woman should display her curves with pride, without camouflaging them. She should allow her natural fragrance to live and breathe, her hands and voice to speak. Her slender, slight body will do the rest. And I foresee a happy future for her.

Why France?

Up until now, when discussing our consumer society and feminism, I was referring to the whole of Western civilization. However, this ideology works best in Northern Europe and the Anglo-Saxon world. Here women and consumption are freer than they are in France.

The taboo on women's curves also exists in their societies but, having observed how different their cultures are, I have reached a conclusion I have trouble confessing – namely, that as far as hating women's curves goes, France holds the record and our mantras and dictates are the toughest and least flexible. French women are the ones who push hardest in the race to lose weight and the ones who suffer most from having curves.

Why are we French in the vanguard of this battle? Having made 'French-style love' and 'French women' into universal archetypes, why do we now want to symbolize the emaciation and disembodiment of these body shapes?

What has led to the taboo on women's curves?

There are two reasons. Our current ideology's fundamental goal was to transform women into consumers. There was not a huge amount of resistance to this in Anglo-Saxon countries, and very quickly women went out to work. France, however, is a Latin country where we are better equipped to resist and therefore to triumph, so this ideology had to deploy its most treacherous and Machiavellian weapons. American women surrendered without a fight, but French women had not been put under enough pressure. They were still naturally too much like women. They had to have their nails clipped and be penalized for their charms. Because our women were the most feminine, they were punished the most.

French women before the Second World War displayed their curves and other signs of femininity, with charm and elegance to boot. Today, after the storm, French women still have a certain aura but their curves have been left by the wayside, and top international filmmakers no longer rush to France to cast their favoured 'sex symbols'.

The second reason is that for a long time Paris was where Western fashion was at, and between 1930 and 1965 our star shone particularly brightly. This meant that when the anti-curve mantras appeared we were the first to be affected and we were the most exposed. At the heart of the transmitter, we heard the message loudest and clearest and, like all good guides, we are still out in front.

Why do we go along with these dictates?

I have just explained to you who, underneath it all, was issuing these dictates. To get our women out to work, our consumer society had to resign itself to granting them new rights. At the outset, feminism aspired to a noble aim which was to fight for equality between the sexes; however, as its militancy grew fiercer and the movement enjoyed success, its programme began to include the eradication of differences between the sexes. From then on, it was no longer about simply being equal but about being identical. All the misunderstandings stem from this and you know the fate that befell women's curves, one of the most wonderful differences there is between the sexes.

So we now know who was issuing these dictates and how, but why do we follow them so blindly? And why are our women so easily manipulated?

Here again I am going to turn to biology, as it is hard to find any field of human behaviour that does not become clearer in the light of its discoveries.

We know that before we even developed into human beings we had been social apes, and for a very long time; which is to say that we lived in groups of fifteen to thirty individuals. There was a relatively strict hierarchy within these groups, which is found in all primates living today, including man. This means that each group is dominated by an alpha ape, the dominant male who is the equivalent of the chief, and then under him comes the number two ape and so on until you get to the weakest of all the adolescent apes, the omega ape.

Physical strength is one of the keys to determining who will be dominant, but it is not by any means the only factor. Aggressiveness, energy and confidence in particular count just as much. The alpha male is the one who imposes his presence on all the others. The hierarchy is very quickly determined. There are a few fights to decide between similarly confident rivals, but once it has been established the hierarchy is no longer challenged and the order within the group is there for good.

In our old, primitive brain structures we still retain a resonance from our primate past. Consequently, we experience the need for a firm leader with the same intensity.

What is more, to these same biological links we owe what we call the herd instinct, which is not the best term to describe it. Fear of solitude is a profoundly human part of our make-up. It has been said that on its own a chimpanzee is no longer a chimpanzee and that like this it would certainly not survive very long. Human beings can live on their own but only a marginal existence and they will never achieve their full potential. American insurance company statistics provide clear evidence for this; men who live alone have a shortened life expectancy and the highest suicide rate.

In behavioural biology, this gregariousness has a more meaningful name, which is the sense of belonging to the group. It is an extraordinarily deep-seated cohesive force that at certain times can overrule our deepest instincts. During the Vietnam War, captured American soldiers were kept in the most extreme isolation so they could be broken through brainwashing.

It is this deeply rooted feeling of being some small part of a whole that drives us to blindly accept any dictates that come from the whole. And here what I broadly call the 50 per cent rule comes into play.

When a flock of jackdaws, migratory birds, settles down for the night at one of the sites along its route the flock sticks together. The birds then spread out and choose their territory. Very early in the morning, as soon as the sun rises, you can sense from very specific signs and special calls that part of the group is ready to move on again. Birds circle round in the air and seem to be calling out to the other flock members.

But this is not enough and the birds most in a hurry try a few false starts. However, the jackdaws only properly take flight once over half of them are up in the air – this is the 50 per cent rule that tips the scales to the heaviest side.

However, it is interesting to note that their idea of the majority is not as democratic as it appears. There are some birds that hold such a powerful position in the hierarchy that their voice counts for far more than the other birds. If the dominant male and the most self-confident birds from the flock are already in the air, then a mathematical majority is no longer necessary. Their presence alone bears a great influence on the final decision.

The same thing happens with human beings with regard to how we absorb dictates, tastes and culture in general. It has been said that theories always start out as heretical and end up as orthodox.

Whenever a fashion emerges, its proponents are often a small group of avant-garde eccentrics. The rest of society does not follow suit and looks upon these expressions of originality with some contempt. However, if this fashion or idea gradually wins support, the main body of the group begins to come round, the idea stops being heretical and this is when leaders start to play their part. In all societies, there are influential or charismatic personalities known for their social impact. They are the ones who take the decisions and make it possible for a fashion to become orthodoxy.

From this point onwards, everyone else gets carried away in the excitement as nobody wants to be left out. This is when our feeling of belonging to the group is at its most intense, and all critical perspective vanishes.

I can recall when miniskirts first appeared in France. They had arrived from England where they were all the rage, but nobody thought they would really catch on with us. A few oddballs tried them out, displaying as it happened some wonderful legs and thighs. However, it was not until certain influential women joined in, thereby encouraging others to follow suit, that all women embraced the miniskirt wholeheartedly.

The same happened with the taboo on women's curves and, although the resistance shown at the time is now well and truly forgotten, to win over the masses an impressive number of top models had to be brought on board. Then the media hammering the message home incessantly, the most famous fashion designers supported by the most experienced advertising executives, certain leading names from the contemporary figurative art scene and the ready-to-wear clothing industry bulldozer all joined together with one voice to bring their immense weight to bear.

I look upon these opposing armies as the ones sending out the dictates and so I will now devote my attention to them.

Who is passing on these dictates?

Fashion trendsetters

We are living in a time when a fashion cannot exist just to please a few select circles as it did in the nineteenth century. Nowadays, culture has become a worldwide phenomenon; it is Western, and when a beautiful American woman falls in love with dreadlocks the whole of the Western world sits in front of its mirror to get the same look.

Media broadcasting has reached such a point that news events are instantaneously flashed around the globe. So, for example, when Princess Diana died, the whole world was in mourning for her. I am not here to discuss whether this is a good or a bad thing, but what does interest me is how a fashion is able to spread so quickly, the channels through which it spreads and who are the people mainly responsible for this. And when I talk about a fashion, I have in mind the one my book is all about, the taboo on women's curves.

Women's curves were of absolute importance to men and then an order dictated by economic necessity decided otherwise. The wicked stepmother summoned her huntsmen and entrusted them with the task of deciding the fate of this favourite. Who were the huntsmen who dared carry out this execution, this crime against nature, without uttering a word of protest? I will introduce them to you in order of the responsibility they bear because although there are genuine movers and shakers, there are also more hangers-on who go along with the establishment. However, all of them have played their part in spreading the dictate.

The number one culprits – top fashion designers

It would be interesting to review the annual collections of top fashion designers and trace the history of how thinness took over. However, this would take far too long and extend way beyond this book's scope. I have looked into this for my own pleasure, and can assure you that these people really do take us into a realm of artistic creativity as they work to produce something new.

Their role is to provide different designs for archetypes that our prevailing culture then selects.

Once women's curves had had their day and designers had grown weary of designing for hourglass figures, they opted for straighter patterns; the whole campaign plan for economic imperatives and feminism had already been decided. To guide public opinion in the desired direction, all the plan had to do was to present what was new.

We could well think that fashion designers were only responsible to a certain degree and that they were, after all, just doing their job. However, it would be hard to overlook the particular flavour and atmosphere that prevail in these creative spheres.

Statistically, homosexuality in haute couture is sufficiently common for it to be considered a factor. A certain number of our most prestigious designers have tastes closely connected with their sexual mores. They are absolutely entitled to this, but when we analyze their designs and what motivates their ideas for fashion it should be borne in mind.

Homosexuality probably brings with it a keen and intuitive feeling for what can be harmonious for women and it is no coincidence that gay men often work in professions where they deal with beauty, hairdressing and interior design. Although they are relatively prevalent in these fields, they are not the only ones who exert influence there.

Yet, however extreme their sophistication and concern for elegance might be, it could be argued that they are bound to be inclined towards female body archetypes that are more android and less contrasting.

We must not forget that women's curves are an extremely sexualized biological signal that is picked up most keenly by a masculine receiver, and I do not shrink from asserting that *the more virile the man, the more sensitive he is to women's curves.* So it was highly predictable that certain gay fashion design circles would not respond as keenly to this sort of message. This was in the nature of things and this is what happened.

What is more, unconsciously, they were tempted to base their designs on women with bodies flat enough to go unnoticed; bodies which could disappear modestly behind the outfits being presented.

But French women are Latin women and shapely with it. Statistically in France, it is very difficult to find very tall women without curves or bosom but with narrow hips, straight thighs and angelic faces. To see this you only need to take a look at the books of top Parisian model agencies.

So foreign models were used, in particular from Sweden and East Africa. Both ethnic types can provide an ample supply of these long, lean, straight bodies, where femininity seems to have found refuge in the purity of the faces.

If such bodies were chosen so wittingly, I believe that it was in part to fit with a certain concept of the female body as android and emaciated. In biological terms, this new morphology is halfway between feminine curviness and masculine angularity. But however valid this reason may seem to us, it only contains part of the truth.

The second reason is perhaps even more fundamental and has to do with the celebrity status and mythology surrounding these designers, who have been made famous as their fashions cross the globe.

Since the end of the Second World War, a profound change has taken place in the way top fashion designers design. *Before them, clothes were created for women. With them, women are created for the clothes.* This seems paradoxical, but having followed how their collections have evolved, this is the conclusion I have come to. All pre-war fashions took the female body into account and designed new prototypes based on its natural shape. The female body was a precious gem for which a beautiful setting had to be crafted, a presentation case to show it off to its best advantage. The gem, like a woman's body, was still the focus of all attention.

Since then everything has changed and changed radically. As regards how design was first understood, we are at the exact opposite end of the spectrum. Such a prosaic and utilitarian task no longer befits these creative princes who must have become somewhat dazzled by the spotlight of celebrity. To them, dressing women seems trivial and they prefer their status of artist in their own right.

This means that they see the new clothes designed this way as *objets d'art*, separate from their function. In the 1950s, when the annual collections were over, the world's most wealthy and beautiful women were willing to pay an astronomical price to be the only ones wearing the prototype, the unique sample.

So it was that deep down in these new designers'

minds, women stopped being important. No longer were they the precious gems, or even the setting or presentation box; now they were a prop that had to be discreet, without any personality, nimble-footed and lithe for the shows but quite shapeless. All beauty was now to emanate from the objects being presented and the slightest intrusion of personality or femininity would cast a slight shadow over the designers' masterpieces.

This was probably how women's curves got outlawed. Designing this way shows a fundamental contempt for women, verging on misogyny.

If, as we say, God created woman, he also created the shape of her body and her curves sprang from his hand. To reject these curves is pure blasphemy and, even when in thrall to the greatest vanity, a human designer can never compete with nature. To strip women of their beauty, their substance and their sex, to entirely claim for oneself all the merit and glory for the designs created, may in part be explained by the dizzying heights of fame and celebrity, which all become even more intense in the atmosphere of haute couture circles.

Men and women are but the two complementary halves of what nature designed. They support each other and the beauty of one is the mainspring of the other.

There are any number of ways to play with the harmony between a body and what clothes it, while bearing in mind that the only thing the scissors should touch in this duo is the fabric. To be carried away by creative vanity or by a particular sexual orientation, and to want to tamper with women's bodies, is to overstep the line of duty, commit the sin of pride and also to confuse in a vague way the part with the whole.

Journalists

As we try to discover who is responsible for sending out these anti-curve dictates, we cannot pass over in silence the enormous resonance chamber that is the media.

The problem we are faced with here is a sizeable one, as we need to know whether journalists are mere observers or actually involved in passing the message on. And, to put it more simply, whether they act as a passive or active filter.

Another even more interesting question is whether journalists should provide their readers with the sort of information they want, or whether the journalist's role should be to stir up the public's curiosity for different information. In other words, should journalists serve up their readers' favourite dishes or give them a taste for unknown foods?

Depending on the answer, the responsibility varies. To my mind, given this alternative, I will opt for the second answer and there are two reasons for this.

Firstly, it is extremely difficult to eliminate all subjectivity from what you want to say. As soon as you take a pen in your hand, you must expect, more or less consciously, to become involved. The value of the message can be inverted just by the tone with which information is conveyed. On the other hand, it is very belittling to act as a passive filter and feed even the greediest readers with fare that holds no surprises. There is an explosive, educational dimension to the role of the press, linked to the number of potential readers. This all goes to show that journalists are in part responsible for what they pass on to their readers.

So who are the journalists who, because of the position conferred on them, have the most impact? Without a doubt, journalists on women's magazines. In France, there are at least a dozen influential magazines that for years have been hammering away the anti-curves dictates. And since then no one has taken it upon themselves to add a discordant note to this chorus of unanimous voices.

I often read these publications because I have to deal with problems that affect women, so the answers they are given concern me too. And sometimes, to my great surprise, I do come across an article where the journalist, weary of constantly holding forth on the same theme, will stop for a moment, out of breath, and voice a few doubts about the orthodox culture that holds sway in the French press. Could women not just let up the pressure for a moment and stop casting anxious glances at their scales or tape measure? The intention is laudable but the tone is not convincing. You can feel the censure weighing down on them. Are they at last actually going to drop the clanger and spice up these boring articles a little? *Will they say straight out that accepting your curves is not enough and you have to love them too?* No, the message that all these women are waiting for in a confused way does not come.

Nevertheless, encouraged by the doubts expressed and the questions posed, you carry on reading and turning the pages of your weekly magazine. Then you come to the emaciated, depersonalized and grim-looking models that always feature there and any glimmer of hope you may have had is extinguished forever.

Most paradoxical are the so-called men's magazines. Part of them is given over to photos of naked women who speak the only language men like and here you will see real women, full of vigour, all shape and curves, with hips and thighs that speak volumes about their power to attract. The fact that the women are naked does not make them more appealing, they would be just as attractive in clothes; when a women has curves you can sense it. And even in this type of magazine, some pages are devoted to women. The latest trends in fashion are presented, and suddenly the language changes: the women are being addressed and once again we are off to some Pacific Ocean beach, accompanied by the same idols, all of them skin and bone, with just enough bosom to stay afloat.

I think that in France journalists have spread the word among themselves and that nobody will dare set the cat among the pigeons, vigorously and without hesitation. But what I am also aware of, because I know a lot of journalists, is that this great moment, an innocent 'night of the long knives', is eagerly awaited, when thinness will face its day of reckoning.

I believe that words get repeated in vain, words over which we linger so long that we end up becoming hypnotized, and everyone is asleep except for women with curves because their curves give them no sleep.

The term 'cellulite' is also a source of great misunderstanding. That cellulite exists, is unsightly, pathological and difficult to live with, all this is true. Brandishing the threat of circulatory problems, varicose veins, stretch marks and ageing skin, I can still go along with that.

However, the major error is not clearly defining exactly who is affected by cellulite. I am convinced that for every ten women reading these never-ending articles, which always appear in spring and summer, eight of them will believe they are suffering from it. Whereas it is highly likely that only one woman in a hundred actually has this type of cellulite.

When journalists are sitting quietly at their desks writing this sort of article, I do believe that a useful message is being passed on in all good faith; however, once it is grasped the message hurts. 'Orange peel skin' is mentioned and immediately hundreds of thousands of hands start pressing down on thighs with such intensity that some tiny, paltry puckering is bound to appear which instantly gets labelled as cellulite. When you are at one end of a chain of information, you are too far removed to hear the despair and misery that revelations of this sort can cause at the other end.

227

Any doctor will tell you about the damage that can be done from reading a layman's medical dictionary. You open it at any page and you will find symptoms of a disease that is bound to kill within three months.

Cellulite is the same thing as beauty cancer. You think you are quietly reading a well-written article and you end up becoming contaminated. And I am talking about serious publications only. I try not to think about the ones that fill up their column inches by peddling unfounded pseudo-medical clichés.

Take, as a striking example, horse-hair gloves, which you see being recommended all over the place. I am going to reveal something rather troublesome. I have been working as a doctor for forty years, and during all this time I have never yet met *a single woman* who was not utterly convinced that a horse-hair glove improved her circulation and got rid of her cellulite. Yet, not only is this untrue, but the truth is that it actually does the very opposite. Using a horse-hair glove, especially a dry one, repeatedly over the skin breaks the skin's mini elastic resistance, causing chronic irritation which can in turn lead to varicose veins.

Try asking your friends one day about what these horse-hair gloves do, and you will be amazed that not a single one knows the truth. And I will say nothing about the role of Gruyère cheese in dieting, which probably contains more fat and salt than any other type of cheese.

And I will say nothing either about not drinking water while you eat. And here I will stop altogether, as it is time to sum up and conclude. There was a message that came from on high, laid down by our consumer civilization and dealing with women's new role in our society. The content was clear: to double overall purchasing power our women had to work. In return, they would be granted an overhaul of sexual inequalities. Militant feminism distorted this message as it drifted from inequality to differences between the sexes, so feminism fought for a unisex. To my mind, from that day on, women's curves lost their right to appear.

And I think that women's journalism has not managed to properly intercept the end part of this dangerous and pointless message.

Ready-to-wear clothing and wanting to dress fashionably

With ready-to-wear clothing we reach what is almost the final link in the long chain transmitting these dictates. Initiative may seem restricted and responsibility limited here, and yet it turns out that as the message crosses over at this level it takes on another dimension, thereby increasing its significance.

If we take a closer look at the variations in fashion, and if we try to find a common thread running through everything the ready-to-wear industry produces each year, we will uncover two influences that superimpose on each other.

At the top of the pyramid are the dictatorial tyrants, the top fashion designers, who can create unrestricted by any material contingencies. This is the refined notion of art for art's sake and stardom. Here fashion sets out the main ideas, what designers call the trend. Nobody questions these edicts which will take fashion down a particular route, whether it be a skin-tight leotard or a floaty creation, simple or baroque. The details are not important as it is the general trend that counts.

Relaying between haute couture and the general public are designers whose independence is curbed by the manufacturers' economic imperatives, and this is where the ambiguity lies. The ready-to-wear clothing industry is in the grip of two motivations that force it in opposite directions.

Fashion designers, given their creative sensibility, are spontaneously attracted to what is new. They each hope to give birth to their own little miracle. However, the industrialists are pulling the other way as their imperative is to sell clothes. They are not bothered about being adventurous: all they dream of is being among the first, if possible, to climb on the bandwagon. However, they are sufficiently clear-sighted to realize that standing still will leave them far behind.

So then we witness these small seesaw variations, simple innovations and attempts to put out feelers and test the public's reactions. Tom Thumb was afraid of getting lost and used his tiny step technique, whereas the very top designers with their seven-league boots show the way.

These minor variations concentrate on details, colours and materials. However, slight modifications that are generally hesitant and careful can land on top of a mine and explode. Sometimes you need only to outline the initial detail of some new direction and suddenly there is enormous demand. You go out fishing for sardines and you end up hooking a grouper fish.

Then, and only under these circumstances do you get the measure of this kind of industry, the market is totally flooded with surprising speed.

The ready-to-wear clothing industry bears its responsibility inasmuch as its designers have never attempted any tiny steps in the direction of women's curves when this was quite possible and definitely profitable. For a creative profession to become paralyzed and deprive itself of some of its potential customers, the ban must have weighed very heavily.

However, this industry bears a far greater responsibility. Not content with excluding women with curves, it took it upon itself to subtly torture them by cleverly playing around with sizes, designs and the style. In practice what this means is that up to size 12 you can dress in the latest innovations that magazines, articles and advertising have presented for you. But if you want a larger size, then think again.

However, to be able to enjoy wearing a certain size, your body has to be put together in the way the manufacturers have envisaged. You choose a size 10 blouse that would fit you perfectly if it weren't for your normal but ample breasts. To accommodate them comfortably, you would need a size 14, but then the blouse would hang loose on you, so once again you feel frustrated.

Lastly, and this goes down very badly, the final outrage is the segregation between those women entitled to fashion and fantasy and those relegated to classic, prosaic and cheerless clothes.

This is indeed what really happens. If you want to dress fashionably your body needs to be flat with few contours, otherwise the designs will not suit you. Wonderfully feminine breasts, hips and thighs bar you forever from wearing trousers, figure-hugging blouses and even T-shirts that look such fun on other people. There is not much left for women with curves; their clothes are either classic or common. Nowadays a young woman with sex appeal can curse her lot dressed either in a slit leopard-print skirt or like her grandmother. As the taboo on women's curves works its way through society, this is the harshest punishment invented.

This excessive zeal was quite uncalled for. Perhaps it does motivate those fortunate women who belong to the 'thin women's club' so there is more trade with them, but it adds quite unnecessarily to the frustration already felt by women with curves.

The cinema

If I have placed cinema alongside corporations that have painstakingly conditioned us with an artificial taste for being thin, then my sole purpose here is to show instead what a shining example the silver screen provides.

Indeed, and probably with more talent than any other industry, cinema could have backed thinness and moulded its idols to fit with our current archetypes. Yet it has managed to retain its independence and in doing so has demonstrated a critical spirit so woefully lacking elsewhere.

With its scorn for the current disembodied female stereotype, cinema has proved that it is possible to be both the *enfant terrible* of one's century and a solid safeguard against decadence.

Nevertheless, there is another more pragmatic reason why cinema has adopted this attitude. When a film director casts a female actress, he knows exactly who his target market is so he is selecting her with his male audience in mind; and it is for this reason that I see the cinema as the living proof of my argument.

From the Second World War up to the present day, take most of the stars who have turned modern cinema into something great and you will be sure to come across a 'sex symbol'. I will never forget the intense shiver that ran down men's spines the world over when Ursula Andress appeared on screen for the first time as she emerged from the water in *Dr No*, the first James Bond film. International critics immediately recognized a sex symbol.

When Bo Derek emerged fifteen years later, for a moment we thought that the same woman was making a comeback. In the meantime, Raquel Welch took away any breath that was left in a hundred million American men.

Take a good look at these three women. What do they have in common with Twiggy, the most famous model of all time?

The role of the actresses, essentially, is to speak to men, not using sophisticated dialogue but with biological weapons: shape and curves being the key words. As for Twiggy, she was meant to speak to women, which is exactly what she did.

The three film stars have the most expressive curves imaginable. You may find some a little bigger or a little fuller but deep down in the rhinencephalon, man's old animal brain, if there is one standard image that can trigger immediate attraction and emotion, choose one of these three bodies and you will not go far wrong.

You can take this image across the ages, wake up the Pharaohs, summon Marco Polo, Casanova or any New York janitor, and their pupils will all dilate the same way and they will all be tempted to reach out with their hands.

When I talk about women's curves, I am talking about the sort of curves these women have, and I can tell you that none of these real women who trigger men's receptors would have stood a chance of working for any one of our top fashion designers. If there is any scandal or a paradox, then that is it; and once again I thank the cinema for allowing me to use this argument.

I am then told in all good faith that any woman would be more than happy with a body like that. This is not true in most cases; you may perhaps want to create as much of a stir, but when you are alone and find yourself in front of your mirror with curves like these, you just itch all the more to be rid of them. I have seen plenty of women in consultations who, without possessing such harmonious proportions, still had thighs and hips that were as fleshy, and they were absolutely convinced that they were riddled with cellulite.

However, cinema did not just bring us these three women. For practically anyone who calls herself an actress, being yourself is a point of honour, which not only reveals men's tastes, but most importantly the fact that not many women have bodies like Ancient Greek adolescent males.

What is left today of this last corner of cultural resistance? It has been invaded by defectors from the world of 'modeldom'.

Those curves that yesterday made us dream have been consigned to the adult film section as this pocket of lucidity and liberty suffers the same fate as the Maldives, and, as it disappears, it takes its splendours with it.

Conclusion

Some of my readers may think that I have gone round the houses to find causes for what is a mere passing fad, and that in this field tastes come and go casually and thanklessly in a way that history has seen many a time before.

If that was what I thought then I would have held back and not written this book, and I would have waited with my arms folded, happy to tell my patients that D-Day was just round the corner.

However, the despair and the pain of living with these curves, which I see every day in my work, is not an isolated symptom but part of a much greater whole, which is about reducing the differences between the sexes, and I believe that I have provided ample evidence of this throughout this chapter. So this is not some phenomenon of little consequence. Once the cultural starts encroaching on the natural, once a fashion starts tampering with our fundamental biological balance, there is no doubt about it – the new thing is decadent and threatens our civilization. And if this civilization is the only one on the planet then our whole species is under threat.

So in itself this taboo on women's curves is an evil but also the symptom of a greater threat. To sum it up plainly, I will say that for a long time progress has been a cultural hypertrophy, providing us with comfort and abundance. It was our idol, a modern golden calf. Today this benign tumour is showing signs of abnormal proliferation. The cultural is turning cancerous and threatening to invade some areas of human nature.

Once we really think about women's curves carefully, we cannot help but realize what an important role they play. Seen objectively, curves are quite clearly the main signal for sexual recognition.

Western consumer society wanted our women and it got them. Over half of them go out to work. To keep them in this new state where only a tiny elite can flourish, they have to be kept 'drugged' with material comfort and feminist ideology.

'The same brain, the same work and the body will follow.' And indeed the body does follow. Men are becoming slightly feminine and women are slowly becoming virile.

The crazy idea of being thin emerged in the 'art for art's sake' atmosphere that reigns in haute couture circles. The message was taken up by women's journalism, then passed on to the clothing and health and beauty industries for them to relay it further. Certain women's publications have gone too far and are responsible for an archetype of extreme thinness and the hysteria surrounding cellulite. The ready-to-wear clothing industry has spread the message on an industrial scale by refining the torture even more with its limited size range, and designs and styles that exclude. This is how the dictate has travelled right along this long chain of specialists who work with women, and at every stage the dictate has gained a little more weight and authority. Once women absorbed the edict, their sense of belonging to the group was so powerful that any critical perspective got swept aside in their frenzied and often subconscious desire to be 'like everyone else'.

This is where we are at today, and there is every reason to believe that this long process of conditioning, which is anything but innocent and definitely dangerous, is not going to die a natural death.

I am certainly under no illusion about any radical change in tastes taking place, even when we are faced with the obvious harm being done.

The problem had to be defined, our eyes opened to it and biological support found for it. Now that this is done, our imperative – and this is vitally important – is to try to go back the way we came and root out ideas and tastes that have become so entrenched that they have submerged the facts.

So now it is time to get on board those people who, by simply being on side, can lend authority, and give them the opportunity to exercise their power.

This is what part three is about.

Part Three

TOWARDS A NEW ERA
FOR CURVES

At the end of this brief biological, cultural and medical overview, I wonder whether indeed I have managed to get my message across.

For you, and a little because of you, I have been able to clear up for myself any confusion there might have been in what was an intuition. Starting out from my medical experience – from dealing frequently with women who are frustrated for no good reason – I have tried to sound a modest warning cry.

If there is one idea I would like to have got across clearly for you to keep hold of, then it is that women's curves are not just about having a bit more or a bit less shape. They are not a mere detail that can be selected according to mood, fashion or season. Quite simply, they are a normal, crucial and morphological characteristic; and one of the four or five signs by which the essence of womanhood is expressed and recognized. This sign is hardwired in black and white into our chromosomes. No other female in the animal world has it, which is why it is our sign and why we must accept it in just the same way as we accept our big brains and our two feet which allow us to be upright creatures.

To any biologist, this is an obvious fact and one we can observe. Yet, whatever the discipline, taking apart and demonstrating an obvious fact is not that easy. Nobody can fully explain the choices nature makes when she selects one organ rather than another.

One of her choices is women's curves, that much is sure – but why? Probably because they are so strikingly obvious and feel so good to men's touch. Nature could have opted instead for colourful lizard-like markings or for smells as she did with certain mammals, or for the sounds that some birds use. But nature opted for curves and we must accept her choice.

Another equally fundamental notion is our reasons for rejecting curves. Firstly, we really do have to admit that the Western world is utterly determined to reject women's curves as if they were foreign matter. If you are in any doubt about this, then you must be living in the back of beyond without radio, television, women's publications or advertising, and you certainly have not tried buying any clothes since the last world war. If this is the case, and even if you have been fortunate enough to have learnt to read, my book will never reach you.

As for everyone else, you have had to opt for the sorry choice – to be naturally without curves or suffer. And if you think you know of cases that fall somewhere between the two then you have been lied to.

I tried to make you see why our consumer civilization was so hell-bent on erasing the differences between the sexes: the most blatant differences, the ones that allow for no doubt whatsoever.

Being thin was dreamt up at the same time as women's purchasing power. Have your own cheque book. Divorce as and when. Take your daily pill, forget all about your curves and go off to work. This is the dictate.

And if you are one of those readers who have followed me right to the end, you are quite entitled to reply that since this is an irreversible choice, what can we do about it? If this amputation is part of social reality and decided from so far on high, there is no point in fighting it.

I will answer you with the word: pollution. By definition, the consumer society pollutes but does that necessarily mean it is inevitable? Every time someone becomes aware of what is going on then more people will reject it. And once we become the majority saying no, we will be the ones with a new truth. It is sad to associate an image as noble as truth with the dreary law of strength in numbers. But this is how things stand and why I am trying to win you over.

I realize that this taboo on curves has been plaguing women all over the Western world, but it is French women who have been following its dictates with most determination. We are perhaps closer to the Good Lord than the saints.

I also realize that this book, whatever its readership, will only have a limited influence because to turn round such a large movement, which has been infiltrating women's collective subconscious for so long, will require an all-out counteroffensive. This is why I am now going to appeal to those very people who have used their influence to hammer these dictates into our minds and ask them to tip the scales once again – but this time in the opposite direction.

What reasons could they possibly have for listening to me?

The first is to do with common sense. Everything becomes worn out, cultural trends and fashion more so than the rest. Even when useful, a way of thinking – a dictate – can change. When it is pointless it has to evolve. If it is dangerous, it must be reversed. And I believe that women have suffered enough and that carte blanche should be given to those people who will go and liberate them, even if at the outset women make an outward show of refusing to be liberated. Asking for help, even if expressed unconsciously, has a certain shame attached to it.

The second reason is based on logical arguments. Our consumer society has achieved what it was after: women work nowadays and are even forced into unemployment. So what then is the point of allowing dictates to persist if they no longer serve any purpose? Give women back their curves, and they will not revert to how they were. Women are not going to give up their jobs and return to the home, so why let them suffer needlessly? A male nutritionist is telling you that women are suffering and this they will never reveal to other men. Why should you not believe him?

So I have decided to write some open letters to those people in power who have enough clout to make us change tack or simply create a climate favourable to a natural mutation: top fashion designers, the media in general, the ready-to-wear clothes industry and its designers, influential opinion shapers. It will be a symbolic open letter, not addressed to anyone in particular and published only in this book.

Before I address these groups, I will appeal to the male sex. There is ample proof that men have distanced themselves from this phenomenon, since the dictate was not aimed at them personally. Somewhat impertinently, the male sex has contrived to allow women to sacrifice themselves on the altar of thinness, knowing full well they would not die from it but that they would lose far more through suffering than they could ever lose through slimming.

8. An open letter to men

As men, you represent the male half of your species. The language I will use with you will therefore be the language of sex. However, there are two ways of interpreting it – for you as adults and for tomorrow's adults, in other words, your children.

Today, you are male because in part you were born that way, but also because you are the fruit of the culture in which you have developed over several decades. So it is important to know not only what you think of your current sexuality, but what ideas you will instil in your children, who so eagerly soak up your every word.

When you hear people talk about women's curves, you may well give a whistle and the impression that you see nothing to take seriously here. You adopt the same attitude when women start talking about clothes. You leave them to it, mildly amused, as you return to your concerns, which to you seem far more serious.

However, I must stop you there. Clothes are perhaps a matter of taste, fashion or season and a plaything that should be left to women. But their curves are a quite different matter altogether.

Without you realizing it, this attribute belongs to you. I will even say that paradoxically their curves belong only to you. And although women carry them, more or less reluctantly, they are merely the guardians.

This signal is an integral part of your retina and your man's fingertips. With some forbearance, we may allow the women we love to discuss this usufruct, but we must never let them squander it.

The human race, like all other species, has been programmed to keep going thanks to our two sexual poles and their eternal game rules. Through a well-established agreement, each pole declares its colour, using a few signs biologically inscribed into its flesh. Women's curves have no other meaning or *raison d'être*. They are probably the most expressive and eloquent sign, and because of this they are untouchable. However, if you want to carry on regardless and undermine their existence, driven by some vague sorcerer's apprentice impulse, you and your partner must take this decision together, in the full knowledge of what to expect.

Try to imagine for a moment how your wife would react if you took the unilateral decision to shave all the hair off your face and body. Quite likely she would think you had exceeded your rights. Yet, women's curves carry far more weight than all your hair put together.

If they disappeared completely, which I hope is not about to happen, one of the most cherished trigger signals for your libido would be amputated.

There are no doubt some husbands, whose wives are devoid of curves, who will assure me that their sexual relations are quite healthy. I have no grounds *a priori* to doubt their sincerity. However, I have to say in reply that perhaps, without realizing it, they are functioning like an engine that sputters away, and they must be intensely virile to make do without such essential stimulation.

But have they thought that what is good without might be even better with? And, most importantly, let's not forget that time erodes the value of messages from a familiar, well-visited body. Faced with such erosion, to keep a hold women should not amputate their best means of creating desire.

That fatal word 'desire' has been uttered. A word we constantly misuse and a word that leads a troubled life in our subconscious. If we only knew what simple materials it comes from!

All males in the animal kingdom assert themselves based on the same criteria and rush to their females in response to signals they obey without understanding. Just because we humans can understand does nothing to change matters. We may understand, but we rush just as eagerly. Only our vanity, which comes from being thinkers, leads us to believe that we could put ourselves beyond a law that is part of life itself.

Biology, as pragmatic as it might appear, reveals a moral code of universal dimension. This code teaches us that love is born of desire and that in essence the bond binding a couple together is an exclusively sexual bond. In the twenty-first century, when everything seems permitted, we are at great risk of forgetting this.

So my message to men is simple and clear. Faced with cultural imperatives, women have abandoned ship and, as they beat their retreat, they risk losing a part of themselves which we men are entitled to. We must provide a counterbalance by taking this apparently benign threat seriously.

Although it seems just like some game society is playing, surreptitiously our sexual relations are being undermined. And our children who, even before puberty, play quite innocently with our scales and tape measures are being programmed with the same bad habits.

If we prefer our women with curves, then it is time to say so and to say it loud and clear.

9. An open letter to leading fashion designers

I would like to start this letter by focusing your attention on a point in part two's analysis that concerns you.

I spoke about the climate of homosexuality that reigns in haute couture circles.

This is purely a sociological and statistical observation; it is most definitely not a value judgement. A doctor or a biologist has no particular authority whatsoever to decide what is good or bad about a type of behaviour, but like anybody else they are entitled to take note of it.

It is widely thought that male homosexuality bestows on those of its persuasion a particular sensitivity, predisposing them to sophistication and hedonism.

Possessing such unique features, gay men interact socially with women with great ease. They more or less have a monopoly over interior design, hairdressing, female beauty and fashion design. Who would dispute this?

However, it is difficult to overlook the fact that the way your personality is structured comes through in your work and that some part of your tastes gets injected into your most sophisticated creations.

Haute couture is one of the fields where you are many. Although you are not the only ones, the high fashion that you serve so well is slanted in such a way that it reflects the dominance of your influence.

Like all creative people, you must have moments of doubt when you question things. So please be patient and listen to me. My analysis of how high fashion has evolved, and how Paris sweeps the world along, proves that the stereotyped norm of lanky bodies populating our leading magazines has been imposed by you. This is an unquestionable sign of your personality. However, if hidden perspectives are implied through actions, this decision, taken in the refined surroundings of your workshops, clearly proves that, for you, women's curves are not an absolute necessity.

Yet, and this is the point I want to make, these curves do have a meaning and a role that you seem to overlook. You may well wish they could disappear from your sight, but a natural invention, millions of years old, cannot be so easily deleted from the biological map.

I know that you have difficulty finding suitable models to present your creations and that very often you have to import them. So the motivation for your choices is not their ease. We need to look elsewhere.

Personally, I have already told you what I think. Feminine charms are not the sort to bowl you over and this subconscious oversight reveals the biological bedrock of your aesthetic design.

What is more, I have reason to believe that these charms get in the way of your creative flights. I have myself heard a top designer confide that it was difficult 'to dress a guitar'. No doubt this is true. A guitar and its curves make demands that have to be respected; the contours are plain to see.

You need to accept second place in creation and humbly admit to being the mere sub-contractor for the master-piece that already exists – women. Women existed long before you came along and you are doubly in their debt for they have given you your work.

Yet I know that you are not responsible for women's frustration. Although I can assure you that only one in a thousand French women are able to actually squeeze into your amazing designs, all you did was put forward your choices; our society took what suited its needs. But given that you are so well placed to suggest innovations, why limit your talents to such bizarrely androgynous designs? Why not embrace the challenge of creating for bodies that actually exist?

I am myself an aesthete, and I can assure you that I feel a great affinity with your taste for beauty, for your creative gifts, and it distresses me to see you neglect the female body which is the very essence of another far greater kind of harmony.

As far as fashion goes, you are what we call the leaders. Most specialist journalists have their eyes constantly focused on you. When you sneeze, the press blows its nose and women put the hankies round their necks. You are the undisputed tyrants of silk and cotton. You decide what goes for the season.

So be munificent, take up the glorious challenge of adding women's true colours to your palette and allow their curves day-to-day freedom of movement.

An open letter to leading fashion designers

This open letter is a request. There is a time for suffering and a time to end the suffering. I think that most women have had enough of being eternally frustrated like Tantalus and we need urgently to work on their behalf.

However, if, far removed from daily reality and the fleshy language of real curves and body mass, you fail to heed this advice and challenge, you will most likely watch a revolution take place without you, and see it come from countries where people can innovate.

Men prefer their women with curves; there is absolutely no doubt about it. Whatever your own preferences may be, it is perhaps time to enlighten your despotism by deigning to glance down at the message conveyed by the statistics.

10. An open letter to journalists on women's publications

This letter is to some extent a formality, since you already know my arguments.

I deem you responsible for having passed on a message that was not your own without subjecting it to any critical examination.

You too have an unusual power, as everything that passes through your 'golden mouth' is disseminated and amplified. You have worn this power away to the point of losing your voice. Through your zeal, women's curves have lost much of their former prestige; there was no need to demonstrate your influence in this way.

Top fashion designers perhaps had the excuse that it was easy for them. By creating designs on shapeless bodies, they avoided the distraction that comes from having a backdrop full of contours. Or, maybe, lost in their splendid isolation, they forgot that a real woman's body is shaped from dough that rises.

But you have no such excuse. You knew full well that the vast majority of your women readers were nothing like the archetypes your articles constantly focus on.

Did you never once think that if one of your readers perhaps managed to identify with the gaunt incarnations that haunt your publications, there were a thousand others suffering to the point of losing their heads? Do you never get letters from these frustrated women?

There is a mystery here I am having trouble unravelling and the only rational reason I can suggest is that, for the most part, you female journalists were just as brainwashed as everyone else.

I have reached this conclusion because you are the ones who perhaps most desperately seek consultations with nutritionists. I have a disproportionate number of your colleagues among my patients, which obviously proves that you are as much victims as torturers.

However, there is one area where you have wreaked havoc. From start to finish, you created the psychosis around cellulite. You have turned a genuine medical condition – unsightly, painful but rare – into something commonplace for everyone. The word has become so widespread that it is no longer used as a medical term but as a concrete noun.

I often ask my female patients about cellulite to see what semantic chord it strikes in women's minds and I have noticed that nowadays the question is not whether you have cellulite or not; the only issue is working out whether you have a little or a lot. This tells us plainly that the psychosis has reached such a point that more or less all women are affected by it.

This is serious and I will tell you why. You have brought the term into such disrepute, loaded it with such repulsion, that a perfectly normal woman suffers more from having a few centimetres on her thighs, judged to be superfluous, than a obese person does from carrying a few extra stone. Paradoxical it may be, but this is how it is. This is not just weight or any old body mass, this is what characterizes the female sex and makes a woman what she is, but you have heaped anathema on it by giving it this dreadful name so as to better fight it.

However, this open letter is not an indictment. We are all of us responsible for the choices our society makes, and the future is of far more concern to me than the past.

Here again, I will draw upon the only authority I have – my experience gained from working as a nutritionist. After treating women patients for many years, I can assure you that those who are completely satisfied, happy or relaxed with their bodies are very few and far between.

What happens at the moment is that the spotlight is turned on any slight imperfection, transforming it into something painful and irritating, while everything else that is harmonious and ought to give women self-confidence gets totally overlooked. This climate of perfectionism leads inevitably to permanent dissatisfaction. There is so much that needs to be done here and you could work wonders.

Once a woman puts down a magazine she has just read she feels doubly frustrated. However bright and colourful your fashion pages may be, they cannot make her forget the models she can never hope to identify with. Your health and beauty pages always unsettle her because you never pinpoint exactly which readers you want to help.

Do you not think just as many women would read your publications if this impression of malaise were replaced by a gratifying vision of womanhood? When women get up early to go off to work, it only takes a small compliment about how nice they look to brighten up their day. Some husbands happily find these simple words that cost nothing, whereas others take a malicious pleasure in putting their finger on some irritating, hidden detail you had hoped might go unnoticed and which ends up spoiling the day.

You are faced with the same alternative, and up until now you have always chosen to point your finger, albeit a well-informed finger, but a remarkably accusing one, at your readers.

Why not try providing a little comfort to all these women, who have coped with such changes in their lifestyle during this pivotal period? Why not display the latest fashions on models with bodies that look more like the average woman? Why do you always have to choose skinny beanpoles who turn common sense upside down and give our women complexes, when it is the beanpoles who should be fretting about their own sorry lack of charms?

Lastly, why keep trotting out the same old recipes and worrying away at them like a dog with a bone? Don't you think it is time to forget about cellulite, or leave it for those women who actually have it?

And your articles on stretch marks, hair falling out, flat feet, sagging breasts and ageing faces? These women all read your features and wonder whether they are meant for them. Aim accurately and leave everyone else out of the picture. You will make all those women who do whatever you tell them so happy.

We say that we cannot be in two places at once. You are in one place and I am in quite another where I can see what you cannot. I talk face to face with the women you converse with in your minds, which is why I have used this open letter to suggest you change course. And I can assure you that most women suffer because of their curves, which they can never have removed because they belong to them. They can be made to lose weight on demand; at a push their cellulite can be treated. But their natural curves are an integral part of their bodies. No one would ever dream of cutting off an arm to lose weight.

Since the 1960s it has been suggested that women should lose weight to get rid of these curves and contours, the symbol and mark of their womanhood. We have not managed to erase their curves but we have managed to give them hang-ups and frustrations undermining the confidence they once had in themselves.

Today, your role is to give them back their lost confidence, their *joie de vivre* and a desire in their minds to be reconciled with these inescapable curves they have found unacceptable. It is a safe bet that the first magazine to dare start this trend will establish itself as a market leader, increase its circulation and, what is more, be hailed as a godsend by all men who love their women with curves.

11. An open letter to the women's ready-to-wear clothing industry

I am also writing to you but without any hope of being heard. This is not because by nature you are any less sensitive than others to the problems women face. But I believe your industry is driven by economics and focuses on production. Presenting you with biological, humanitarian or aesthetic reasons serves no purpose. So let's talk business instead.

And immediately I make the surprising observation that there is a women's ready-to-wear clothing market for which you are the sole official suppliers. For reasons for which you are not responsible, three very distinct types of female consumer can be distinguished in this market.

The first group is the stereotypical fashionista, who at the first signal is ready to follow the slightest twists and turns of fashion. She was born to be in the vanguard. Whatever her age, she is young in spirit. She cannot be said to have a very strong personality, but she is jolly, carefree and often pretty. What is more, she easily identifies with current female archetypes. These women are few and far between and make up only a small part of the population.

A second group brings together women who are traditional and have resigned themselves to giving fashion a miss altogether. They still harbour vague regrets about this but prefer now to look upon fashion as some rather frivolous oddity. This is how things stand for mothers; serious and solemn, they always look a bit older than they actually are.

Most of these women have curves they hide away and which are usually the reason behind their early retirement from fashion. They form the silent majority.

'Coquettish' women make up the third group: 'sexy' women who have curves and are proud of them. They know full well that their curves are an asset, especially in a society where most other well-endowed women no longer dare show them. So they use and abuse them, so much so that they can end up being rather vulgar.

Very ample bosoms in tight-fitting tops bordering on the indecent, hips and thighs squeezed into a sheath, all far more revealing than any bikini, and there is provocation in the air.

You know your market far better than I do and no doubt your marketing experts have been studying these three categories of women for a long time. But it is not at all clear to me why you have decided to plough your efforts exclusively into the smallest group. All your advertising budgets, your designing and investments go into what is new and risky and all for the first group of women.

Is it because their purchasing power largely offsets the other groups? I doubt it.

Are you aware that traditional and 'sexy' women have problems finding the right clothes and out of desperation they wear the same horrors or the same frippery?

I know this argument will not persuade you, but I cannot help but tell it like it is for these suffering women. The one group endures in silence, deliberately opting for the 'old-fashioned'; the other shouts in their own way, preferring to play with its assets and use what little you so parsimoniously make available.

I already know what your answer will be, as I have put the question before to people in your sector. You are not responsible for these archetypes, and I grant you that. You did not impose these emaciated, sexless bodies on us, this much is true. You regret the way things are; that this modest scruple troubles you is hard to believe, but I do want to believe you. But then how do we explain the whole systematic codification with inaccessible sizes, designs that only fit the lucky few and styles that mostly exclude the unlucky, which amounts to nothing less than a refined form of torture that segregates and isolates most of our women? You give the impression of being a private club that recruits its members from circles where morphology deviates from the social norm.

Do women have to keep on trying to be ever thinner so as to be able to dress decently? And if concerns for egalitarianism are totally eclipsed by your businessman's pragmatism, why does the law of numbers not influence your economic concerns?

As for your market, your marketing and market development, you have neglected most of your female customers. A simple effort of imagination, allowing your designers a little free rein (and they are just waiting for the signal); a few extra centimetres in the right place, clothing that is loose or tight to follow the movement of normally proportioned bodies. In brief, by looking at women through fresh eyes, you will attract plenty of new customers who will be unable to believe what they are seeing. If among you there are some men who can still remember bedchambers and who are fond of enlightened profits, let them join forces and make sure they inject some new life into an industry sector that is starting to stagnate in its own dreary orthodoxy.